There was once a

So the woman let the ocean sing her soft lullabies and hold her gently, till eventually she fell asleep in her watery bed. All night the ocean mother held her child and kept her safe.

Thirteen Shamanic Stories

by

Manda Clements

First Published in Great Britain in 2011
by
Sound of the Heart Publishing

Digital Imaging and Layout by Silver Moonlight
Covers by Miça Wellwood of MetaPhorce

A CIP catalogue record for this book
is available from the British Library

ISBN 978-0-9547302-3-9
Sound of the Heart Publishing
c/o Cilgraig
Capel Dewi
Llandysul
Ceredigion
SA44 4PP

To order further copies of this book, please see page 156

Printed and bound in Wales by Gomer Press, Llandysul, Ceredigion

Michaelmas font courtesy of Dan Zadorozny of Iconian Fonts
Goodfish font courtesy of Ray Larabie at Typodermic

Dedication

In memory of my Dad, George,
who taught me that asking questions
was a great way to learn what really excited me

and

for my children, Tom and Anna -
my best teachers

Contents

List of Canvases

Introduction

Wow! Think what it would be like if we all fully embraced being the heroines and heroes of our own stories. Brave souls, journeying through the inner landscapes of our own tender, vulnerable wounds. Courting the assistance of our own magnificence and remembering to let life tickle us at every opportunity.

Of course we all are the heroines and heroes. Life is the adventure and the giants and goblins we meet along the way are the grit that creates the pearl.

Our stories matter. They are the telling of our innocence -original sense- incarnating into physical life, to experience this beautiful planet.
Our stories are creating our shape. By owning our stories, we place our vulnerability into the powerful hands of self responsibility.

Shamanic journeying is a fabulous tool to ride through those inner landscapes. The delicious wisdom, fragrant with truth, served up in simplicity, with a flourish of joy, is the flavour I've savoured there again and again. But how can it be a feast if it serves only one? And so I've painted these journeys in words and colour and call you out to play in the wild garden of our natural souls. There I will show you the most precious of places. They are the spaces I've left, into which I invite you to weave the threads of your own stories. The cloth created tells of the big adventure. The wandering fool, who's being welcomed home, into the outstretched arms of their own divinity.

There are several ways for you to enjoy this book

 Take some time to snuggle down and have a good read of the stories.

 The invitations are there to assist your own story to unfold

 The paintings can be used much like inspiration cards. Allow the image to help reveal the opportunities or choices of your present time.

 Or you may wish to share this book with a group of others, using it as a catalyst to deepen your connection to your individual and collective stories, to inspire your own creative adventures.

Hidden within the stories of all women lies the story of the Goddess.

There was once a land
where children were
persuaded to trade
their beauty...

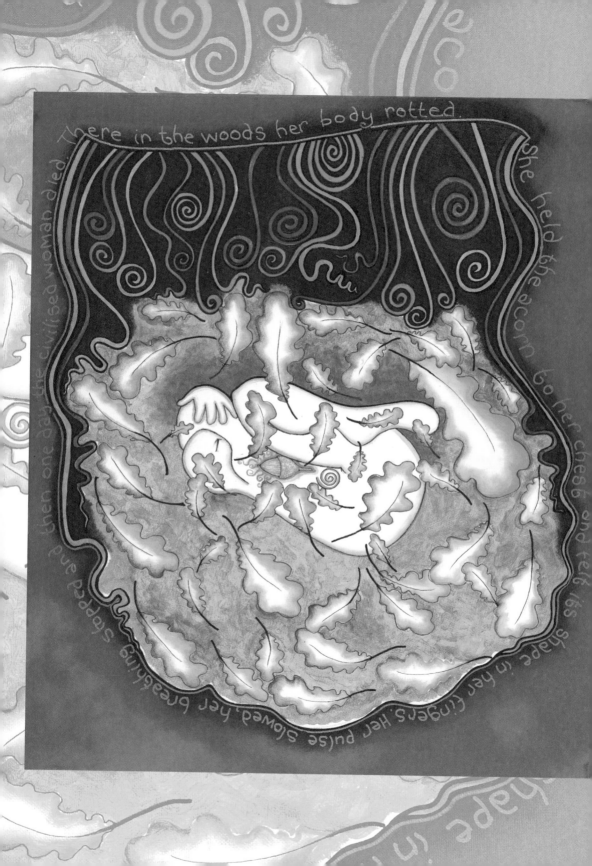

There in the woods her body rotted. She held the acorn to her chest and felt its shape in her fingers. Her pulse slowed, her breathing stopped, and then one day the civilised woman died.

Introduction

When I moved to west Wales, it was to start a new life.
The only trouble was I didn't actually know what that new life
was to be about. I rang up a shamanic counsellor, who lived an
hour's drive away, and asked for her help in working out
the meaning of the move.
We worked together over about four sessions.
The theme that came up for me was about beauty.
For me, beauty is the truth of who we are.
I also knew that my relationship with my own beauty was
distorted and disempowered.
The following story was from the last shamanic journey made in
that series of four. I asked for the power to create structures in my
life so that I could express beauty.
This story continues to unfold, petal by petal, as life challenges me
to explore, ever more deeply, the truth of myself.
Having trained as a teacher, and worked with under- fives whilst
my own children were young, I watched with great sadness
children giving away their aliveness, their uniqueness, in order to
fit in and not rock the boat. This politeness, this niceness, can be
a poison that eats away at the wild child, the wise child, the child
that feels the heartbeat of the Earth and knows how to live
harmoniously with it. I've had so much to learn from such children.
Innocence and authority need to be in a loving and respectful
relationship. I needed to stop being afraid to dance to that great
rhythmic beat and I needed to stop being afraid of death.

There was once a land where children were persuaded to trade their beauty. They were persuaded by those who loved them, those who felt ashamed and awkward in the presence of the wild, natural souls of their own children.

At first, the children held on, defiant, but nearly always there came a time when each child felt the heavy burden of shame, and the gift of their uniqueness became too heavy for them to hold.

At this point they would reach inside, looking for the place they held their gift, and place it into the waiting hands of those who loved them. In exchange, they received a smaller, colder, harder gift - the gift of uniformity.

On this day, a celebration was held. Those that came feasted hungrily on the wild, untamed beauty. They ate it raw, until the blood dripped off their chins and fell to the floor, but they always mopped it up afterwards with serviettes - after all, they were a civilized people.

The child would feel affirmed in its citizenship to this place - how could it leave now? It had given its beauty in payment for being there; now it could make its parents proud and be just like them. But inside, they felt the gnawing emptiness that the small cold gift could not fill. Only when they became parents, and feasted on that which they took from their own children, would that emptiness be temporarily filled.

Children were born and grew until they died, bonded in the conspiracy of beauty docking.

It was into this land that a girl child was born. Life spoke to her in soft whispers and its voice made her smile.

Then the voice was deafened by the intrusion of others. Others that knew not how the vastness of the sky made her spirit soar or what walking barefoot on the earth could teach or how the rhythms of the world danced inside her. Others that knew not the lushness of moss or the songs of flowers, the kiss of the wind or the cry of a free heart. So wild was this child that those who loved her feared she was oblivious to the shame she brought them - so intoxicated by life was she - whereas they had only known children that had been docked. Nobody had ever told them how ugly a child could be before it had been civilized. It was a secret that the people of this land held.

But the child lived outside, and there, bare footed on the earth, she knew who she was. The rhythm of the Earth sang to her and taught her her song. She sang it to the trees, the wind, the sun and the creatures that crawled through the earth.

Then a day came when shoes were put on her feet and she was taken to a place that was not outside - a place where they did not feel the world through their feet. A place where they were told what to do and when. Nobody sang her name to her and nobody heard when she sang it to them. She felt for her gift, but now she felt for it shamefully. She reached for it when nobody looked, and as her fingers touched the petals of her exotic bloom, she felt her heart ache as she realized how far inside her gift had receded, in fear of being found, in fear of being docked.

Day after day, the girl struggled on. She screamed and kicked and tried to get away, but always she was brought back.

Eventually, the burden of carrying such rare beauty became too much. So, once more, she reached inside until she felt the dewy touch of the petals of her exotic flower, her wild indigenous soul.

She held it in her hands before holding it out to be traded. The grown-ups feasted hungrily on it, not noticing how the child stood holding her small cold gift of conformity.

That was the day a piece of her soul broke off in grief.

That was the day when life became easier in so many ways but one: How to stem the hunger her conformity could not feed? The cleaned up, tamed and sanitized version was insubstantial.

Her parents, however, breathed a sigh of relief. They had worried that they were bad parents - but now, their child had been civilized.

They knew they had done their duty by her as responsible parents. After all, they did love her so.

The child grew into a woman with the smile of conformity on her lips, but the grief of her mutilation was always in her eyes.

Now the smile was for a memory and a deep yearning to be back in the rhythmic silence.

One day, the woman had a child and she loved it. But it made her heart ache, and she knew what it was that she needed to feast upon.

Her child also fought the docking.

So, slowly, the woman sucked it from her child, just a little at a time. One day, she looked up and saw the blood trickling down from her chin - the sight shocked her.

What was she doing? But she gnawed so inside - was there no other way? Then, to her surprise, she heard the voice of that part of her soul which had left her all those years ago. But at this time, the woman didn't even recognize it as part of herself, so outcast a life had her lost soul lived, so hideous, so gnarled and twisted had it become.

She feared her own soul, but she also could not trust her civilized self. How could she, she who had given up her most precious gift, how could she know what to do?

and as her fingers touched the petals of her exotic bloom, She felt for her gift but now She heard She felt for it shamefully. She reached for it when nobody looked

"What have I done?" the woman cried.

"You've survived." her soul replied.

"But at what cost?" the woman asked.

"You've given your beauty into the hands of others. Placed it outside yourself for others to consume. Now, like them, you have become a consumer of beauty. Ravenous, you search for it in the things you do, in the life you take with those others.

"That part of you which once held your beauty is now traumatised. It sits in a corner, rocking, holding the empty wrapping of a memory now fragrant with grief. Neglected, it waits awkwardly in the institution of conformity, muttering of loss. This part of you is your truth. It remembers your beauty. Look at your truth, however painful that may be. Don't gloss over it. Sit with it. Let it teach you the song it has been muttering. Now is the time for you both to start singing the beloved back."

"But I don't know the song," the woman replied.

"You knew it once, now you have to remember it."

The woman spent a long time remembering her song. She took off her shoes and walked barefoot on the Earth. She felt a distant pulse and a sense that a memory was making its way back to her. She made time to watch the crawling things in the earth and to be kissed by the wind. She re-learnt the songs of flowers and stroked the lush moss. Slowly, the feeling of her returning song grew.

She lay down in the woods and covered herself in a duvet of leaves. She held an acorn to her chest and felt its shape in her fingers. Her pulse slowed, her breathing stopped and then one day, the civilized woman died.

There in the woods, her body rotted and she became food for the acorn she held. As her energy seeped into the ground, she at last realized what scared her people - the wildness of its children's beauty that smelled of exotic dew-touched flowers also smelled of death. To be fully alive, one must also fully accept death.

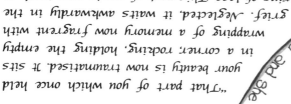

One day the woman had a child and she loved it.

The small, cold gift that was lovingly put into the children's hands had been the gift of immortality. They had tried to tame their own true natures so that they could tame death. But in fearing death, they never truly lived.

Now, the woman's body becoming compost - the food from which the new seed would grow.

The moulds and insects helped break her down, releasing her from the illusion of separation. She was no longer hungry, now it was she who was the food.

The acorn split and a new shoot, nourished by the rich compost, pushed itself above the ground. The woman's energy moved up through the roots and into its first quivering leaves.

How easy it had been to die. But now, through this new oak tree, she felt the pain of being born. Once the tree had been a part of everything. Now, as it became visible, it risked everything. The push to become visible was so pressing, so eagerly did the leaves reach for the sun.

Now the woman understood courage - it was being born. She felt the flurry of excitement that drove the plant on and she heard the song that was singing it into life.

But she was not the oak sapling up through the leaves she travelled, and felt the kiss of the sun. She became the golden light around the leaf. The flutter of excitement grew as she moved from the leaf, merging with the shafts of golden light that filtered through the trees.

It was then that she heard it, remembered it - her song. As she heard it, she found herself being reborn as a forest child, a wild woman-child.

Now, when she looked at the gnarled and twisted piece she held the acorn to her chest and felt it... in her fingers. Her pulse slowed, her breathing stopped and then, one day the civilised woman died. There in the woods, her body rotted.

the acorn split and a new shoot pushed itself above the ground The woman's energy moved up through the roots and into its first quivering leaves. But she was not the oak...

Together now, they would sing her orphaned beauty home and give it a place to live – safe inside where she could touch its dewy petals.

the memory of her song pushing to the surface.

trying to defeat it. She welcomed her guardian to her, and as they merged she felt every part of its shape told the story of how it had flowed with life, rather than rain and wind. It had not grown tall and straight, but it had grown uniquely and

Its shape was like a beautiful piece of wood that had been with the elements of consumed by those who loved her.

It had shown her how to embrace her truth, so that her uniqueness was not

It was the guardian of her beauty.

of her soul that had left and returned she saw the beauty of its integrity.

Forest child,
Free and wild.
Touch the wind,
Kiss the sun,
Golden one.
Forest child,
Free and Wild,
Forest child.

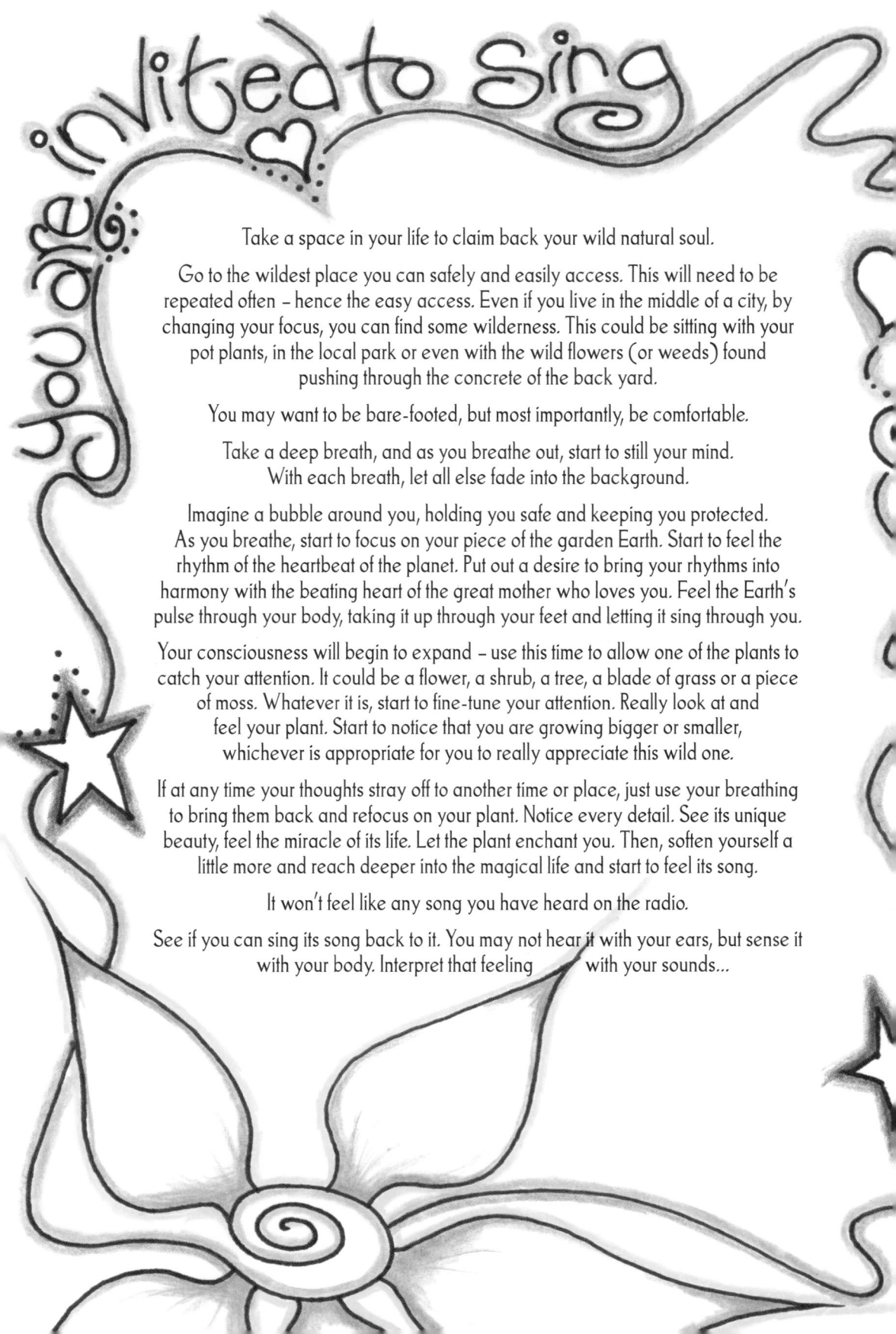

you are invited to sing

Take a space in your life to claim back your wild natural soul.

Go to the wildest place you can safely and easily access. This will need to be repeated often – hence the easy access. Even if you live in the middle of a city, by changing your focus, you can find some wilderness. This could be sitting with your pot plants, in the local park or even with the wild flowers (or weeds) found pushing through the concrete of the back yard.

You may want to be bare-footed, but most importantly, be comfortable.

Take a deep breath, and as you breathe out, start to still your mind.
With each breath, let all else fade into the background.

Imagine a bubble around you, holding you safe and keeping you protected.
As you breathe, start to focus on your piece of the garden Earth. Start to feel the rhythm of the heartbeat of the planet. Put out a desire to bring your rhythms into harmony with the beating heart of the great mother who loves you. Feel the Earth's pulse through your body, taking it up through your feet and letting it sing through you.

Your consciousness will begin to expand – use this time to allow one of the plants to catch your attention. It could be a flower, a shrub, a tree, a blade of grass or a piece of moss. Whatever it is, start to fine-tune your attention. Really look at and feel your plant. Start to notice that you are growing bigger or smaller, whichever is appropriate for you to really appreciate this wild one.

If at any time your thoughts stray off to another time or place, just use your breathing to bring them back and refocus on your plant. Notice every detail. See its unique beauty, feel the miracle of its life. Let the plant enchant you. Then, soften yourself a little more and reach deeper into the magical life and start to feel its song.

It won't feel like any song you have heard on the radio.

See if you can sing its song back to it. You may not hear it with your ears, but sense it with your body. Interpret that feeling with your sounds...

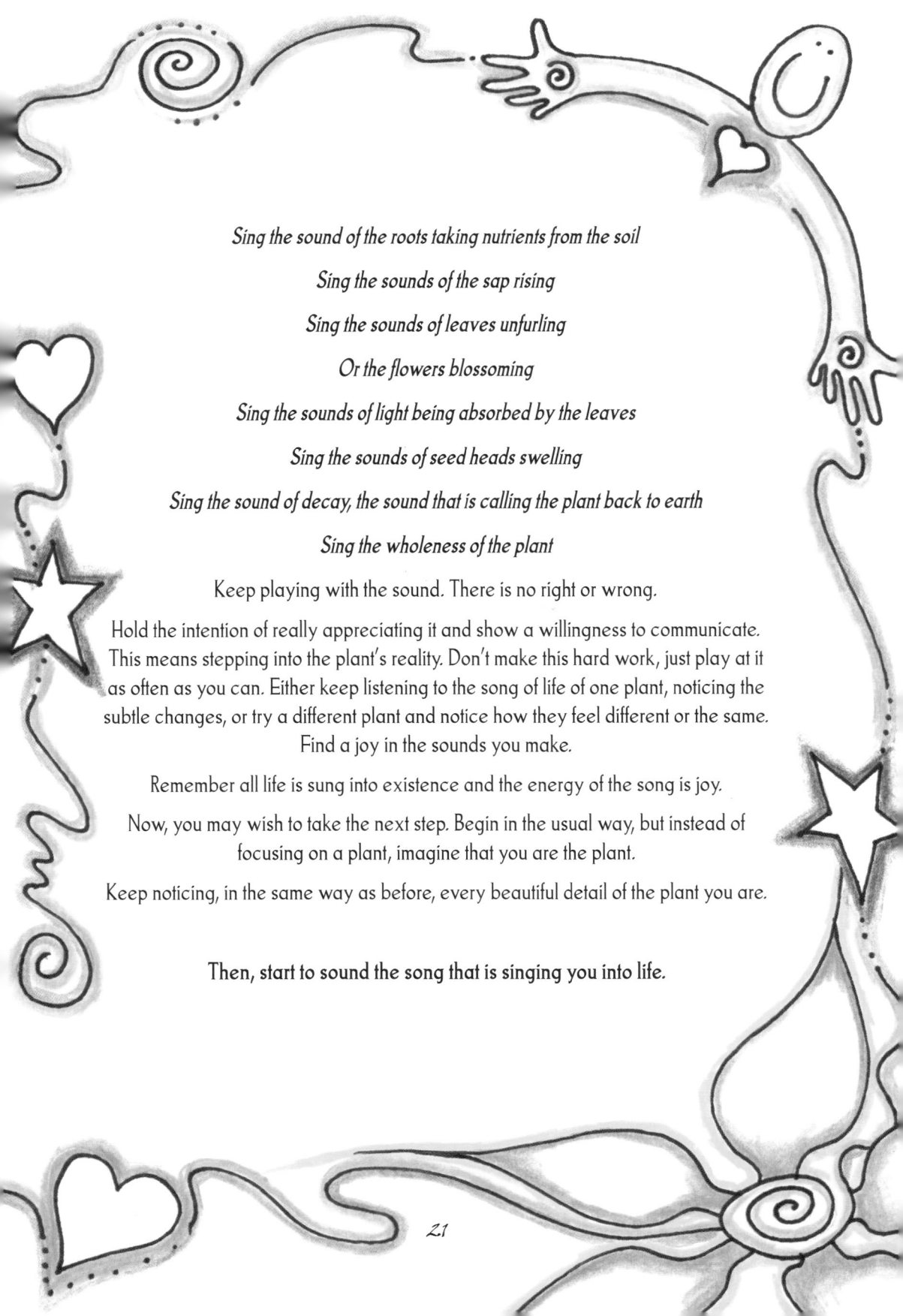

Sing the sound of the roots taking nutrients from the soil

Sing the sounds of the sap rising

Sing the sounds of leaves unfurling

Or the flowers blossoming

Sing the sounds of light being absorbed by the leaves

Sing the sounds of seed heads swelling

Sing the sound of decay, the sound that is calling the plant back to earth

Sing the wholeness of the plant

Keep playing with the sound. There is no right or wrong.

Hold the intention of really appreciating it and show a willingness to communicate. This means stepping into the plant's reality. Don't make this hard work, just play at it as often as you can. Either keep listening to the song of life of one plant, noticing the subtle changes, or try a different plant and notice how they feel different or the same. Find a joy in the sounds you make.

Remember all life is sung into existence and the energy of the song is joy.

Now, you may wish to take the next step. Begin in the usual way, but instead of focusing on a plant, imagine that you are the plant.

Keep noticing, in the same way as before, every beautiful detail of the plant you are.

Then, start to sound the song that is singing you into life.

There was once a woman
who decided one day
to visit the
Queen of Heaven...

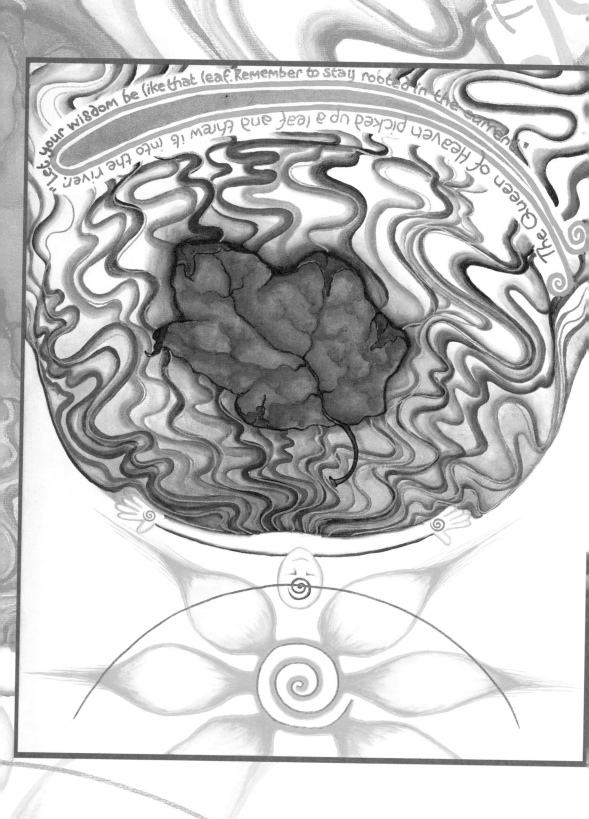

"Let your wisdom be like that leaf. Remember to stay rooted in the current." The Queen of Heaven picked up a leaf and threw it into the river.

Introduction

The question for this next story arose from doing a card reading for
myself using Isha and Mark Learner's "Inner Child Cards".
In the reading, one of the cards talked about "The Queen of Heaven".
This really caught my imagination and I wondered who she was.
As usual, this idle wondering took me to a place I never expected
and the wisdom of this story is one I refer back to again and again.

At the time, I was feeling particularly adrift, mostly because my
spiritual journey was not grounded in any established path. I'd been
told very early on that I would create my own path – this was part
of my soul's journey. This has been very difficult at times and I'd look
enviously at established spiritual communities whether they were
Christian, Buddhist, Druid or any other form.

My path has been to acknowledge them all, and not to be
exclusive to any. All spiritual paths are rooted in the same Earth
and have grown fed by the same Sun.
The diversity of all of these paths is a wonder and it is the places
where they touch or overlap that are the most interesting to me.

But the vulnerability of walking your own path is that
at times you have to ask "What is my wisdom rooted in?"
At the time of making this journey, I felt confused and vulnerable
and was seeking something strong and protective to hold me.

However, the strength I was offered turned out not to be as expected
- but then that's the great thing about journeying – sometimes you find
you already know the answer, you just don't think you do.
At other times, you think you do know but actually you don't –
this was one of those times.

There was once a woman who decided one day that she would like to visit the Queen of Heaven.

She wasn't sure how to get there but she knew it would be a journey into the very core of her being. She asked a tree to help her. Up she climbed, up and up until, eventually, she was so far up that all she could see were leaves and clouds.

She was tired now, but as she looked up there was still a lot more tree to climb. Just as the thought crossed her mind that maybe, just maybe, she would never be able to get there - wherever there was - a large hawk flew down and grabbed her by the scruff of her neck.

It was to these bright points of light, that the Hawk was flying

Up the hawk flew, much faster than she had been able to climb, until stars began to appear, and when she looked down, the Earth was far below.

She was worried now about the hawk - surely this was too far, even for a great flyer such as she.

At that moment, her attention was caught by two bright stars. They seemed to be travelling towards her. As they came nearer, the woman saw that it was to these bright points of light that the hawk was flying. As they met, the lights wrapped themselves around the tops of her arms so that she looked like she had armbands made of light.

The hawk was now free to return home. The woman thanked her - she knew that without the help of the hawk, she might still be halfway to somewhere. They parted as friends. Off flew the hawk, and off flew the woman on her star light armbands.

She danced and glided through the heavenly bodies until the woman, giddy with dancing, realised that they were coming close to a planet that shone with golden light.

Closer and closer she came until she was floating around the top of a great mountain.

Even the mountain was golden, shaped like a giant cone. It was there, right on top of the giant golden mountain that she touched down.

As soon as her feet touched the ground, the two bands of light unwrapped themselves from her arms and stood before her.

For the first time, she could see that they were like two small children, but made entirely of light. She watched as they shimmered and twinkled before her.

"Have you come to help me find the Queen of Heaven?" the woman asked the star children.

At this, they giggled together and once again, wrapped themselves around her arms and flew her down the mountain, spiralling down the golden cone, until they landed on a huge bridge.

The two star children stood and watched as the woman studied her surroundings.

Far below the bridge, a great powerful river cut through the rocky terrain. Mountains climbed to the sky to both sides and everywhere was golden. It felt golden and wild.

"Which way?" she asked the children.

"Either way" they replied.

To the left, she saw some movement amongst the rocks and boulders of the river bank. So to the left she went.

As she got closer, she could see a woman standing at the water's edge, washing her sheets on the rocks. She asked the stranger woman if she were the Queen of Heaven but even as she said it, she knew that she was.

28

The Queen of Heaven smiled and asked why the woman was surprised to find her here - washing sheets.

"Did you expect something more splendid? More magnificent?" she asked.

The woman laughed as she pictured the Royal throne and majestic ways of the Queen of Heaven she had conjured up in her mind's eye.

As she watched now, she saw how perfect this woman was, here, in the wildest of places, doing the everyday chores that women throughout time and space perform. Here she found the Queen of Heaven.

She jumped from the rock she had sat on and asked if she could help. Together, they folded sheets and put them in a basket. The woman then asked the question that burned in her heart, the question that was the reason for her making this journey.

"How can I be rooted in my wisdom?" she asked, "I feel so adrift."

The Queen of Heaven picked up a leaf and threw it into the river. The river received it and took it into its flow.

"You want to be like a tree on the bank, solid and well rooted to the earth?" the Queen asked. "But why not let your wisdom be like that leaf. The leaf surrenders. It lies back and allows the river to take it on its journey to the sea. To be like the tree, you have to watch the river run by you. To be like the leaf, you can lie back and enjoy the ride.

"Sometimes you'll see the blue sky, sometimes stars, sometimes forests and sometimes wide open spaces, sometimes cities and sometimes the very shyest of creatures; sometimes you'll see that tree you want to be, and will watch it disappear again. And maybe, just maybe, this time you'll go all the way

"Let your wisdom be like that leaf. Remember to stay rooted in the current... picked up a leaf and threw it into the river." The Queen of Heaven

and reach the sea. Remember this," said the Queen of Heaven and she looked at the woman in such a way that the wisdom of eternity glowed in her eyes:

"Remember to stay rooted in the current."

The woman looked for the leaf. It was already on its way. She saw that if her wisdom was that leaf, and she struggled against the current, then all she would see was the struggle. And in that moment, she knew she wanted to see the many things the Queen of Heaven had told of, especially the quiet and private places where the very shyest of creatures played freely.

Free from her burning question, the woman was now able to be nosy.

"Why did I have to travel so far to find you?" she asked.

"Why do you think?" replied the Queen of Heaven.

"Is it to show how disconnected I am from you?" answered the woman.

The Queen of Heaven laughed in a way that showed the woman how dearly she was loved.

"I knew you would say that," the Queen replied.

"No, it was to show you how big you are.

"At the moment, you don't realise your magnificence, but that doesn't stop you being so. The coming of day does not stop the stars from shining. When you have learned to be rooted in the current, then you'll have time to connect with the stars. You'll discover this for yourself, but don't worry about it: be fully in your life and be guided by your intuition. Even in surrender, the leaf only sees a little on either side

"At the moment you don't realise your magnificence but that doesn't stop you being so,"

of where it is, what's
around the corner is
round the corner. The
only sure thing is that
the sea is the end and
another beginning of
the river's journey."

The two women picked
their way through the
boulders of the shore
and made their way to
the home of the Queen
of Heaven. Together,
they hung the sheets on
the washing line to dry.
Soon it was time for the
woman to leave. They
embraced.

The woman felt how
glad she was to know
this was the core of her
being and that she was
always here.

Before she went, the
Queen of Heaven held
her in her arms and
looked into her eyes and said,

"Be co-operative with yourself and you will be amazed at what your journey brings."

Then, she called to the star children, who wrapped themselves around the woman's arms, and took her into the air.

Back through space they danced into the arms of the Earth. Hawk was there to see her back safely to the foot of the tree. She sat there for a while, the tree pressed against her back. Then, smiling, she walked home.

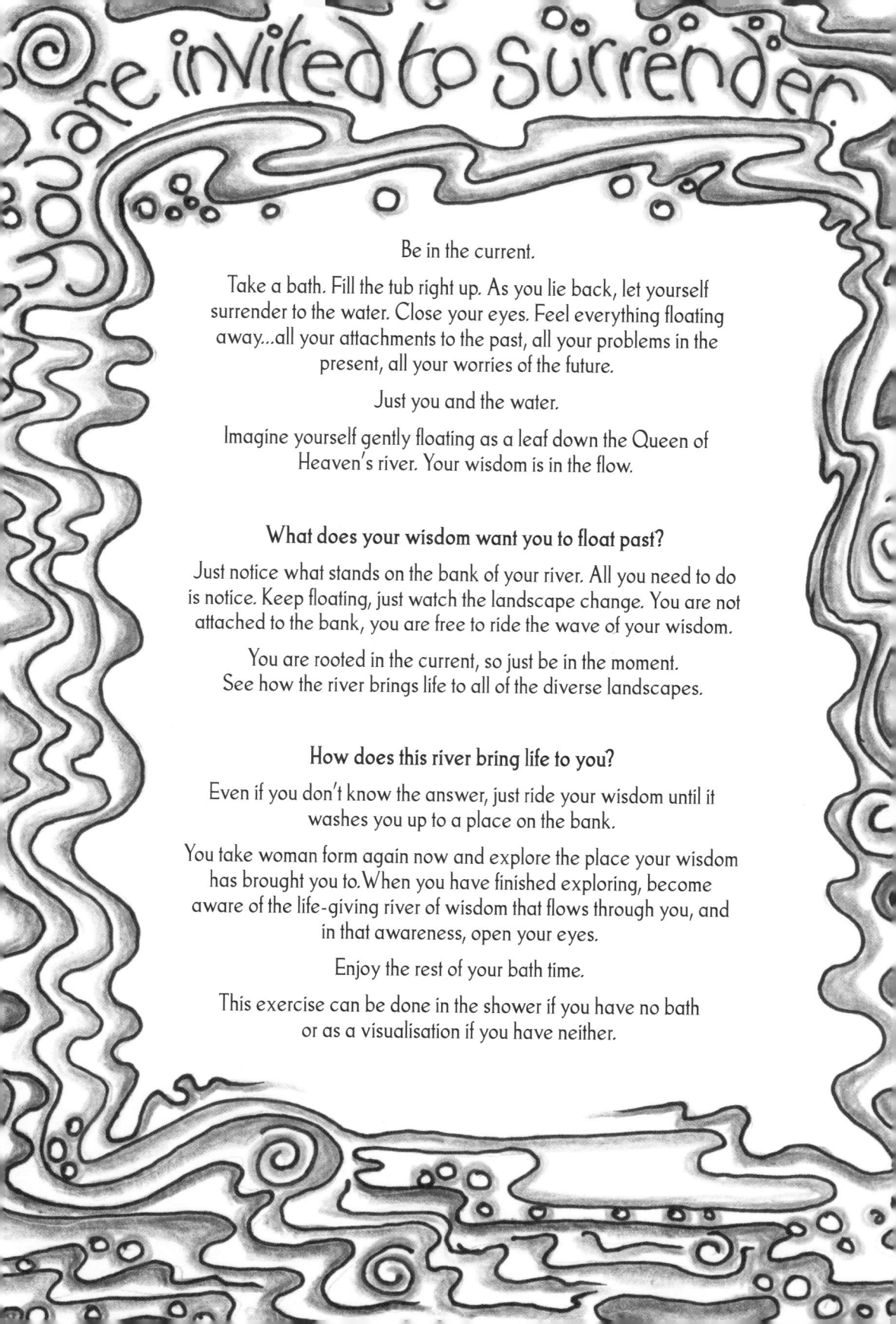

...are invited to surrender.

Be in the current.

Take a bath. Fill the tub right up. As you lie back, let yourself surrender to the water. Close your eyes. Feel everything floating away...all your attachments to the past, all your problems in the present, all your worries of the future.

Just you and the water.

Imagine yourself gently floating as a leaf down the Queen of Heaven's river. Your wisdom is in the flow.

What does your wisdom want you to float past?

Just notice what stands on the bank of your river. All you need to do is notice. Keep floating, just watch the landscape change. You are not attached to the bank, you are free to ride the wave of your wisdom.

You are rooted in the current, so just be in the moment.
See how the river brings life to all of the diverse landscapes.

How does this river bring life to you?

Even if you don't know the answer, just ride your wisdom until it washes you up to a place on the bank.

You take woman form again now and explore the place your wisdom has brought you to. When you have finished exploring, become aware of the life-giving river of wisdom that flows through you, and in that awareness, open your eyes.

Enjoy the rest of your bath time.

This exercise can be done in the shower if you have no bath or as a visualisation if you have neither.

What is
the New Age?

Introduction

There is so much talk about "The New Age".
It's one of those things I had presumed everyone knew the meaning of.
The next story was prompted by me wondering whether I thought
I knew or whether I'd actually just jumped on the bandwagon.

"The New Age" sounded such a hopeful, inspiring concept that I
really hoped that there was something coming up that would give us all
a chance to learn from our mistakes and start again with the benefit
of hindsight. And if this new beginning had a kick up the backside
from the Universe to get it going, then all the better.

This journey was done on a whim,
a casual sort of pondering, with the realisation that I had a tool
(altered state of consciousness journeying) to investigate it.
I don't know what I thought I'd get from the journey,
probably cosmic talk about the angle of the dangle
that would all sound over my head.

What actually happened was quite different.

For a long time, I wouldn't show anyone else this story as the simplicity
of it was extremely challenging for me.
Especially the "Accept you're God" bit.
Now, these are the very bits I love the most.

We are all journeying together, and whatever the angle of
the dangle is, I find just accepting paradox, keeping it simple and being
the creator of my life is the most empowering way to be.

Mhilst walking through the fields, past her tree friends, a woman was wondering exactly what the "New Age" was. She'd heard the phrase many times in many different contexts and wondered what her part in it was.

She climbed her tree and before long, found a staircase going up into the clouds. Hawk was flying around and the two friends greeted each other.

As she stepped onto the stairs, they started to move and became escalators, taking the woman far into the sky. She hoped to meet the Queen of Heaven as she knew she would be able to ask her dear friend all those things that puzzled her.

Up she went further into the blueness. Hawk came and settled herself on her hand.

She hoped to meet the Queen of Heaven.

The woman met the bird's golden gaze; she smoothed the feathers and felt the muscular body beneath. As hawk flew off, the woman watched in admiration at the power and agility in flight that her friend displayed.

She rose through the sky until she came to the very edge of the Earth's atmosphere. There a car waited for her - it was like the sort you see on a fairground big dipper. The woman climbed in and off through space she flew; looping the loop, swerving and curling until they arrived at a sandy planet. The car landed and the woman got out. She watched as the car turned into a point of light and disappeared into the sky.

Striding towards her now came a giant of a man. He picked the woman up and placed her onto the top of a giant golden cone mountain. The woman had been here before. The giant was now at eye level and she looked into the man mountain's face. She felt the familiarity of this place - something inside felt at home and knew it belonged.

The giant showed the woman how to fashion a mat from the grasses that grew at the mountain's top and, on this, the woman slid down the mountain, helter-skelter style, landing with a bump on the veranda of a riverside house.

She sat on the balustrade and watched a small fishing boat come towards the house.

The woman jumped up as the boat neared - she had recognised the skipper.

The Queen of Heaven threw her a rope with which to moor the boat. She passed the woman a basket of fish which she had caught. The woman looked at the gold and silver beauties that filled the basket.

When she looked up again, the Queen of Heaven was by her side and the two women went into the house.

They sat together at the table and gutted and cleaned the catch. Whilst they worked, the two women caught up with what had been happening in their lives. It was so easy to be in the presence of the Queen of Heaven. So completely did the women feel her total acceptance. Eventually, the woman asked her question:

"What is the New Age?"

"Well it's not whizzing around space as you've just done."

The two women laughed at the absurd way the woman had arrived.

"It's this," the Queen of Heaven said, gesturing to what they were doing.

The woman looked around at the simple abode. The two of them sat at the table preparing food, the easy natural feel of the place and the tasks.

"It's simplicity," she carried on, "Doing everyday things simply."

The woman asked many more questions. She was used to a life of complexity and she had much to untangle before she could comprehend the fullness of the simple answer.

The Queen of Heaven listened, but refused to let the woman push her into complicated answers.

As the woman tied herself into further knots, in an effort to untangle the puzzle of simplicity, the Queen of Heaven added:

"The New Age is about knowing who you are - God. Then doing everyday things in that knowledge. If you really knew that you are God, and so is everything else, then how could you harm yourself or another?

"It takes great courage to announce this message to the world. To many it will sound egotistical, but it isn't. If you knew who you really are, really knew, then that would be it. Life would be made simple, and all you would have to do is to know how to make it even simpler. Think about it - how would you live your life knowing that you are God, and so is every one and everything else?

"But instead, you feel small and insignificant so you make your presence feel large and complicated. If you knew how large you really are, then you would stop shouting to be heard and would find peace in your heart."

The woman thought of her life. She knew that feeling of smallness and insignificance. She remembered the ways she puffed herself up just as she'd seen her cat do when faced with an enemy. But like her cat, there was no substance to her posturing, just bluff and hoping nobody would know that what lay behind it was just little old her - afraid that the world would beat her up, like a bully picking on the weak and feeble.

She thought of the people she admired - those that seemed to be doing important work, complicated work, too complex for her to fathom. She asked her friend about this.

"They still need to keep it simple, and if they knew they were God, it would help."

The woman recognised how humbling an experience being God was. It seemed like a paradox that the mightiest are in fact the simplest or humblest.

Her mind started to knot itself around the notion of paradox. Her mind enjoyed tumbling around the complexities of paradox's puzzle.

But it was a maze, and every time she thought she was near to solving the puzzle, she'd turn the corner and find herself journeying the other way.

She worked hard at the trickiness of her thoughts and didn't notice the furrow that appeared between her eyes. The puzzle had started to creep across her face.

She was brought back by the Queen of Heaven's light touch as she brushed her hand across her brow.

"Just accept paradox for what it is," she said. "Stop trying to make straight lines where there are none. Paradox is part of life. To make your life simple you just have to accept that."

The woman shook her head to bring her wandering mind fully into the present. As she did, the worry lines fell from her face and she smiled at how hooked she was on complication. But now was her chance to be simple to be with an expert.

She turned back to the fish, some of which were being fried in a pan. She smelled the delicious smell and enjoyed the rising feeling that all was well in the world.

As they sat together eating, the woman asked about her life and her plans. The Queen of Heaven allowed herself to be drawn one more time:

"Strip away all that is unnecessary. Be God. Accept paradox."

Then she carried on eating. The woman knew the subject was closed. She smiled to herself as she ate her fish.

The temptation to add clutter was a temptation she found hard to resist. But instead of being hard on herself, she just found it amusing. She was God, but she couldn't accept that yet and something about the space between the two made her smile. She knew it was inevitable that one day she would accept that was what the New Age was all about, but for now, she accepted the paradox that she knew, but she didn't know.

you are invited to be God.

Know you are God.

Make yourself a badge that says "I am God" and wear it next time you
do your housework. Clean the toilet as God. Vacuum the floor as God.
Sort out your rubbish as God. Make your home clear and clean as God.

If you forget and fall back into the little you, look at your badge,
remind yourself and carry on.
Take your tea breaks as God. Balance rest and work as God.
Delight in your work. Sing as you go. What would God sing?
What would God have for her lunch?
At what point would God say, "That's enough," and do something else?

Then go and do something else.

*There was once a woman
called "Heavy Shoulders"...*

Introduction

The birth of this story was at the women's circle I used to belong to.
We would take it in turns to meet at each other's houses,
on the new moon, using Jamie Sams' book 'The Thirteen Original
Clan Mothers' as the inspiration for each session.

The woman in whose house we met would provide
the framework for the session and each of us would
have read the relevant chapter in advance.

It was June – Storyteller's Moon.
We were asked to sit in silent meditation for a while to contact
the story from our lives that we needed to share at that time.
The seed of this story came from that space of silent reaching.

When I got home, I meditated further upon the unfurling story
before writing it down. It is my story of giving up my job running a
pre-school play group, then turning my attention to decorating right
through our house, leading up to us selling to move to the place
where I could engage with the next level of my soul work.

Yes, looking back, it all sounds a bit lofty.
But I suddenly heard myself asking for this move at the end of a
sweat lodge and was told it would take two years to manifest.
In the meantime, I had work to do.
And boy, did I make hard work of it.

I dream, I realise, my heart still beats.

Note: in Native American traditions, the coyote is the 'trickster', a
being who can give advice, but the advice is often given in such a
way as to lead you in, seemingly, the wrong direction.

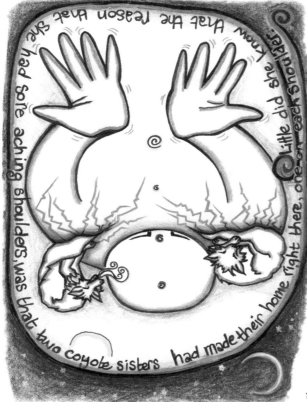

There was once a woman called "Heavy Shoulders". Every morning she would wake, hoping to be free of her soreness. But each morning, the stiffness and aching in her muscles reminded her of the burdens she carried. So she would get up, rub her aching muscles and get on with her life.

Little did she know that the reason she had sore, aching shoulders was that two coyote sisters had made their home right there, one on each shoulder. There they lived and practised the things that coyotes do best. How they loved to trick poor Heavy Shoulders. They took turns to whisper in her ears. They always finished each bout of whispering with a conspiratorial wink, other than whispering and winking, mostly they slept.

Caught between the two whispering coyotes, Heavy Shoulders was led the meanest of dances.

Eventually, she believed she could do nothing right. It was at this point of despair that she decided that she would do nothing, and by doing nothing, she wouldn't be able to do anything wrong. So she gave up her job and waited for her aching to heal.

But of course, she didn't know that she had two coyote sisters living on her shoulders!

The first coyote stood up and whispered in the woman's ear:

"Now you're not working, not contributing to the running costs of this family, the least you can do is give this home the love and attention it so needs. Clear out the rubbish, decorate the rooms to reflect who you are. Honour your creativity and your journey by creating beautiful healing spaces for yourself and your family. Then you can be proud of this time of 'doing nothing'."

Little did she know that the reason that she had sore aching shoulders, was that two coyote sisters had made their home right there, one on each shoulder.

With that, the coyote winked at her sister and settled herself down for a well-earned nap.

Heavy Shoulders set to. She cleared the rubbish and dreamed her dreams of the beautiful spaces she would create. Spaces full of love, light and beauty. Spaces that spoke of who she really was. Spaces in which her family could find peace, healing and inspiration. Spaces in which they too could express their creativity. A space for her family to be together and honour who they were.

Heavy Shoulders dreamed big dreams. She allowed her creative expression of her dreams to start work. She worked hard at 'doing nothing'. She worked with passion at 'doing nothing'. She worked with growing confidence that she had been right all along in 'giving up work, and 'doing nothing', she could not go wrong.

Now the second coyote started to wake from her sleep. She saw how much Heavy Shoulders had managed to achieve. But she could also feel the tiredness Heavy Shoulders was starting to feel. In fact Heavy Shoulders felt it was now her time to slow down, to run with the ebb and flow of her energy, to quieten herself to re-engage with her dream, to reflect, to recuperate. To walk in the sunshine, talk to the trees, sing to the long swaying grasses. To open herself up to the vastness of the sky, to acknowledge the beauty that was everywhere, held in the millions of tiny miracles that happen every day. Then she would gather all this into herself, ready to let it out in the next phase of her work.

But the coyote sister also knew of her thoughts, and so she stood up and whispered:

"You lazy, self-indulgent woman. Your family needs their beautiful spaces. How can you create them by walking in the sunshine appreciating beauty? That's not how walls get painted or floors sanded or curtains get made!

"Do you really believe opening yourself up to the vastness of the sky, whilst your husband and children toil, is a justifiable existence? It is nonsense, it's just an excuse to shirk your responsibilities, to be lazy and self-obsessed."

Well, what was Heavy Shoulders to do? Although her shoulders ached more than ever, and not just her shoulders but her back, her arms and, most particularly, her hands, she turned back to her dream and on she worked.

After winking to her sister, the second coyote settled herself to sleep.

The first coyote sister bided her time. She watched and waited. Then, one day, when Heavy Shoulders was taking a break, up she got and started to whisper:

"Look at you," she said. "Are you stupid? You can't even do 'nothing' properly. You want to be a wise-woman but you can't sit still long enough, you really are too stupid ever to be wise."

Heavy Shoulders was dismayed. She knew straight away the truth of this. She had thought she could not get 'doing nothing' wrong. But she had forgotten what a stupid lazy person she was.

And so again, she started to do 'nothing'. This time she hoped she would get it right. But she really did just do 'nothing'. She didn't walk in the fields, or sing, or paint, or allow herself to play. She just sat.

In her head a muddle grew, and it grew and it grew, until one day she cried out, "Oh how hard it is to get 'nothing' right. If I'd known how hard, I'd have stayed at work - life was easy then."

But she knew that life always gave the perfect lessons needed to grow.

Then one day, as she sat very quietly, she suddenly became aware of the two coyote sisters. She started to understand what had been happening.

She felt their weight and heard their whispering. Worse still, she saw how they winked to each other.

She saw how well they knew her and how cleverly they had taught her of her lack of self-worth. How effortlessly they had knocked her off balance. She started to smile at how easy she made their game of trickery by never doing things just for herself.

Now it was to herself she turned. It was now that she heard a voice that she had not heard for a long time. The more attention she focussed on the voice, the louder it became. It was the voice of her own heart.

Anchor these whisperings to me and I will balance them

It was the voice of her own heart.

"My sister, if in doubt, it is always to me you must turn. I will not trick you. Do not be hard on yourself; you have already seen where that may lead. You carry wounds on your shoulders and it is in these scars that the coyotes have made their home. They, in their own way, have been true to you. They have shown you how you regard yourself. How you long for balance but instead overcompensate, swinging one way, then the other.

"Anchor these whisperings to me and I will balance them. Let me show you the miracle of beauty that you are every day. So many things you have done with good heart, but bring balance to every action and then you can never truly be wrong.

"Thank your coyote teachers, but brush them off your shoulders. Choose not to be Heavy Shoulders any more. Remember that the beautiful healing spaces are inside each of us. Let yours shine out.

"But remember: coyotes are like dogs. When you shoo dogs off a sofa, they will find a way of sliding back up when you are not looking. The two coyote sisters will be the same. Their tricks will always be their gift to you, but you may have to brush them off many times and re-find me. If this is so, do it with thanks and enjoy your homecoming. It is only when you truly do everything for the love of yourself that those coyotes will really take notice. It seems easier, or even more noble of you, to think of your husband and, more especially, your children first, but it is only when you do it wholly for yourself that you will find your wholeness."

And so Heavy Shoulders brushed off the coyotes. The sisters slipped away, winking to each other and wondered how soon they would be back.

Light Shoulders knew that as there are cloudy days, there would also be days when her own light would be clouded. That she would wake once again with heavy shoulders. She realised she needed to see the sisters as visiting teachers whom she could, and would, ask to leave as the sun broke from behind the muddle of her clouds. This would not be failure, but rather a journey of learning, and what she was learning was to be loving, most especially to herself.

If she wanted to create beautiful healing spaces, they had to be allowed to grow inside of herself and be given birth to. Then they would truly reflect who she was, rather than be compensating for her muddle. But she also needed to love her muddle and her aching shoulders because they were the human part of her on the journey to being.

And what of those coyotes? They find they have much to do in the world and are forever on the lookout for those they can teach through their trickery. You may have heard their whisperings, or maybe not. But if you can see them on another's shoulders, be sure to look on your own.

you are invited to nurture yourself ☺

This is a free ticket for you to take the space for yourself,
to do whatever your heart tells you that you need to do.

**Time out for _____ to be completely selfish
and in so doing, become more loving.**

**Permission is given to ask for the help
needed to make this happen.**

**This ticket gives the bearer the right to
indulge herself fully in her heart's desire.**

This is a magic ticket and can never run out.

Make a list and keep working your way down it.

Keep adding to the list – go wild.

For example:

Have a bubble bath with scent and candles

Have a lie-in

Put your favourite music on

Go on an outing of your choice

Have your favourite meal for dinner

Wear your best clothes for today

Phone someone you love

Say NO to something you don't want

Say YES to something you do

Be in the company of the friend that you can laugh with the most

Tell the truth to yourself

Take a step towards making a dream happen

Be a non-practising shy person i.e. do something
brave you didn't think you had it in you to do

There was once a woman
who felt she had forgotten
how to be...

Introduction

The first ever shamanic journey I intentionally took to the
below world was where I shape-shifted into a seal.
Seal has been one of my soul teachers, my heart teacher ever since.

This particular journey was made during a shamanic course. I can't
remember what our teacher asked us to do. All I remember is that it was
a journey to the below world. This is a place to connect with the energies
of the Earth for the purpose of, for example, healing or gathering power –
not the power to manipulate or exert over another, as is often the context
we hear this word used in, but to gather power much as an acorn does –
holding the power to become an oak tree – power in its uncorrupted form,
empowering us to take our true form.

I was on the course to formalise my relationship with altered states of
consciousness – 'journeying', sometimes called 'shamanic journeying'.
Journeying is just a tool – the ability, in itself, does not make one a shaman
– I would never presume to call myself such because I certainly am not
– but I do use this tool to help me to expand my understanding of my life,
to gather power, to heal, to connect with wisdom, retrieve teachings and
seek vision of future possibilities. I also use it in workshops to help the
group connect to a place blocked to them in ordinary consciousness and
so expand their ability to empower themselves. It sounds complicated,
but really everyone does this all the time
- when dreaming, when losing oneself in a film or a book.
The tool of journeying is harnessing this natural ability.

Back to this story. I asked the question 'How can I be?'
because so much so-called 'new age' stuff is about 'just being'.

What the heck does that mean? It's not that I don't believe that this
was what was needed, I just didn't understand 'how to'.

So this journey was made to answer a very basic question asked out
of sheer frustration. The answer cut across all the grown up angst to the
simplicity of the innocent and made me really cry.
Not tears of sadness, but tears of tenderness and joy
that melted my own heart.

There was once a woman who felt that she had forgotten how to "be", so she decided to go for a walk and see if she could find someone to help her.

Off she went, across the fields near her home, until she came to a tree friend of hers. She sat by the tree and poured out her heart. The tree replied that its branches stretched high into the sky and its roots deep into the earth. It would help her to search out someone who may be able to help. The woman sat against the tree, shut her eyes and allowed the tree to begin its quest.

The next thing she knew, she had fallen into a small hole at the base of the tree. Down amongst the roots she journeyed until, eventually, she came out the other side.

The other side was a hill near a sandy beach. The woman was fond of the beach and the sea looked inviting. Across the sand she ran and dived into the water.

Now she was starting to feel her sense of "being" return. The water soothed and restored her sense of self. Worries were washed away in the lapping water and her body felt alive in its salty lick.

The woman was so enjoying the water that she hadn't noticed a seal swimming with her, mirroring her movements. If she went left, the seal went left; if she bobbed beneath the surface, so did the seal.

The woman enjoyed this game of follow my leader. Then she decided it was time for her to follow the seal. The seal took her to a place where the seaweed fronds danced in the water and rolled her body in their tickling fingers. The woman copied her.

What deliciousness. Both now danced with the weeds. A sensual dance, a dance to get lost in - such pleasure - such joy.

The woman didn't know how long the two of them played in the seaweed's arms, but eventually they moved away in search of a new game. The woman asked the seal if she would show her how to 'be'.

"I have been," replied the seal.

The woman laughed and knew this to be true. They swam some more, the seal diving down and catching fish. Then they swam to the beach. They lay, allowing the sun to dry and warm their bodies. The seal, full from her fill of fish, dozed off. The woman watched her sleeping. Watched her whiskers as her breath went in and out. Watched her beautiful friend, tired out from playing.

The woman got up after a while, and wandered back down to the sea. She walked in and lay back in the arms of the ocean. She felt the water mark scribbling along the length of her body. She listened to the under-water sounds, as gentle waves rocked her.

She looked to the sky and enjoyed being supported by the water.

This is the reality of how I am held by Mother Earth, she thought.

I am one of her many children; she holds me in her arms and rocks me. She lets me suckle at her breast and allows me to find how to take my wobbly steps in the world.

But always she is here to hold me...

To comfort me...

To remind me I am her child.

As the woman's thoughts drifted away, she realised that more time had gone by than she thought.

Now, the sky was dark and the moon was out. The ocean seemed huge and she felt tiny, and in her smallness, she felt very afraid, very lost and very alone.

But at that moment, the spirit of the ocean whispered in her ears.

The ocean introduced herself and told the woman that, indeed, she was huge and it was she who held the woman and she was a very capable mother:

"Lie back, my child. Let me rock you. Let me soothe away your fear. Trust me, don't be afraid."

The woman lay back. She allowed the ocean to take her in her arms and rock her.

But soon, waves of fear rocked the woman. She imagined the enormous creatures that lived in the ocean, creatures for whom she might be a tasty snack, but the ocean calmed her again:

"Think of how large I am. Even the biggest of the creatures are dwarfed by my vastness. Remember: it is I who hold you. Not one of those creatures is mightier than I. Be my child. Let me be with you through this night."

So the woman let the ocean sing her soft lullabies and hold her gently, until eventually she fell asleep in her watery bed.

All night, the ocean mother held her child and kept her safe.

By morning, she delivered her back to the beach. The woman woke to feel soft sand under her body. She moved further up the beach, relieved to be back on dry land.

She realised that she was treating the sea with fear, like an enemy she had fought and survived. She felt ashamed as she remembered how tenderly this vast mother had held her.

The crab showed her its cumbersome shell and giant front claws, it asked her to admire them. always ready for battle with this armour.

This water was not an inanimate object. It had whispered comfort to her and brought her home.

She went back to the water and cried her tears of shame and thanks. She asked what gift she could give in appreciation. The ocean mother once again whispered to her:

"Remember the sacredness of all water and find ways to bless it."

The woman sat a while longer, between the worlds of the sea and shore, allowing the sacred moment to be shared.

Then back to the beach, to warm and dry herself. As she went, a small crab passed her by. She lay on her belly to ask the crab if she had anything to tell her about how to 'be'.

The crab showed her its cumbersome shell and giant front claws and asked her to admire them:

"I'm always ready for battle with this armour," the crab told her.

"What about when there are no battles to fight?" the woman asked.

But the crab's mind was elsewhere. She had invested too much energy in maintaining her protection - how could there be 'no next battle'? Because the crab had her armour, off she went to look for her next fight.

The woman lay down in the warm sand, sifting it between her fingers and toes, watching the hundreds of grains, every one different, all coming together to make this beach.

She was startled out of her daydream by the seal's return.

Seal had been watching her. Now, together, they played until suddenly, a deep knowing bubbled up inside the seal - she loved this woman - she loved this seal.

They lay together on the sand. The woman drank the seal in, becoming drunk on the intoxicating love she felt.

She felt the seal's breath on her face, as she breathed in and out. As she snuggled in closer, she felt the tickle of the seal's whiskers. She started to laugh, but her laughter turned to tears; tears of joy and tears of pain, in equal measure.

She had made this journey not knowing how to 'be'. In finding out, she now wept for all the times she'd been too busy to play.

As the noise of her crying subsided, she noticed Seal's huge, loving eyes gazing into her face:

"Keep it simple," Seal said, "and always be open to let life tickle you at every opportunity."

Back to the sea, the two friends raced.

Back to the seaweed fronds and their tickling fingers - what a delicious time they had.

All too soon, the woman knew that she needed to return to her home. She needed to find how to let life tickle her, and knew that she had a friend and teacher to return to if ever she needed to be reminded.

I journeyed to my teacher
With serious intent
For a serious lesson
Earnestly meant.
And was told...
"Let life tickle you at every opportunity."
As the rain pours
And the wind whips your hair
Find a kind of deliciousness there.
And shout to the wind
"Dance with me here"
Then dance the dance
Of letting go fear.
So, whenever I sit
With serious intent
Let me remember
Just what that seal meant.
Let me sit lightly,
Free from the weight
Of earnestly waiting
For clues to my fate.
As life tickles me now
Let it tickle again,
An ecstatic dance
With a wild woman's grin.
Has she gone mad?
In the wind and the rain?
Or is it that life is tickling again!

you are invited to play

For me, Seal sits in the south of the medicine wheel – the place of the child.
Children's work is PLAY.
They know best how to 'let life tickle them' at every opportunity.

Take a child out to play. If you have young children, then great,
if not, you may know of someone who would love a couple of hours off.
If you really can't think of any young child that can accompany you,
then you can take your own inner child out to play.

Think of a place to go. The park, the beach, the swimming pool, your own kitchen
table, or even under the kitchen table - anywhere that appeals to the child within.

Make a play date. You are not there to enable the child to play whilst you hold
coats, pushbikes etc. Oh no, you are their play date.

Swing on the swings, dig in the sand, enjoy the sensuality of the water,
make a mess on the kitchen table
(cornflour and water mixed together makes a great gloop to drizzle and mess with).
Make a camp under your table and make a feast to eat in your camp.

It doesn't matter what you do; it's the quality of getting lost in the play,
engaging with your spontaneity and letting your imagination get tickled.

Follow your joy – sing, laugh. Nothing has to be done well and only do what's fun.
Discover your body as your best play tool. At some point,
lie still and really feel held in the arms of the great mother who loves you.
Lie as her child, cherished and blessed in her arms.

Make a gift for her. Pick some flowers, sing a song, turn a cartwheel, make a
pattern. It's not what you give, but the love you put into it.

Be as silly as you like on your play date. Your responsibility (ability to respond) is
to feed your joy and find freedom by letting go of 'should do's and 'ought to's.

Measure success not in what you achieved but in the fact that you gave
yourself the time, space and permission to play – well done!

A woman had a dream...

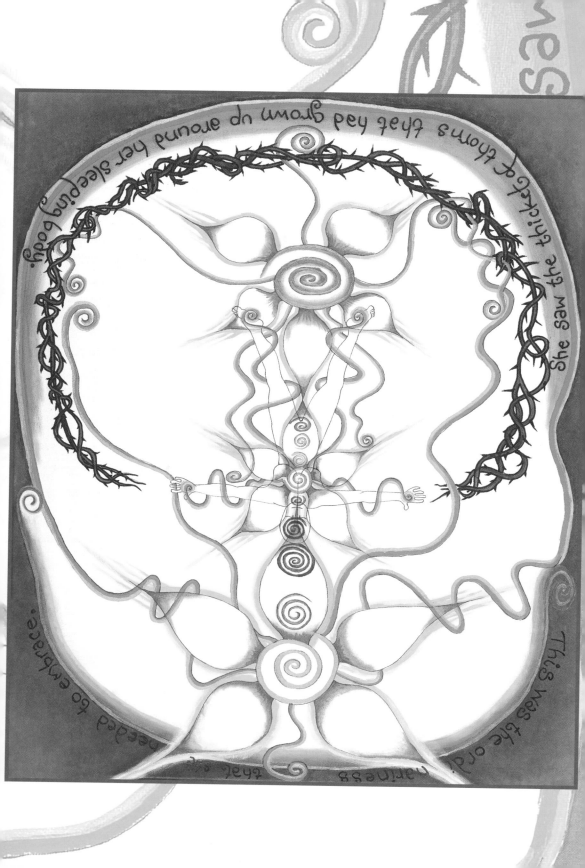

She saw the thicket of thorns that had grown up around her sleeping body. This was the ordinariness that she needed to embrace.

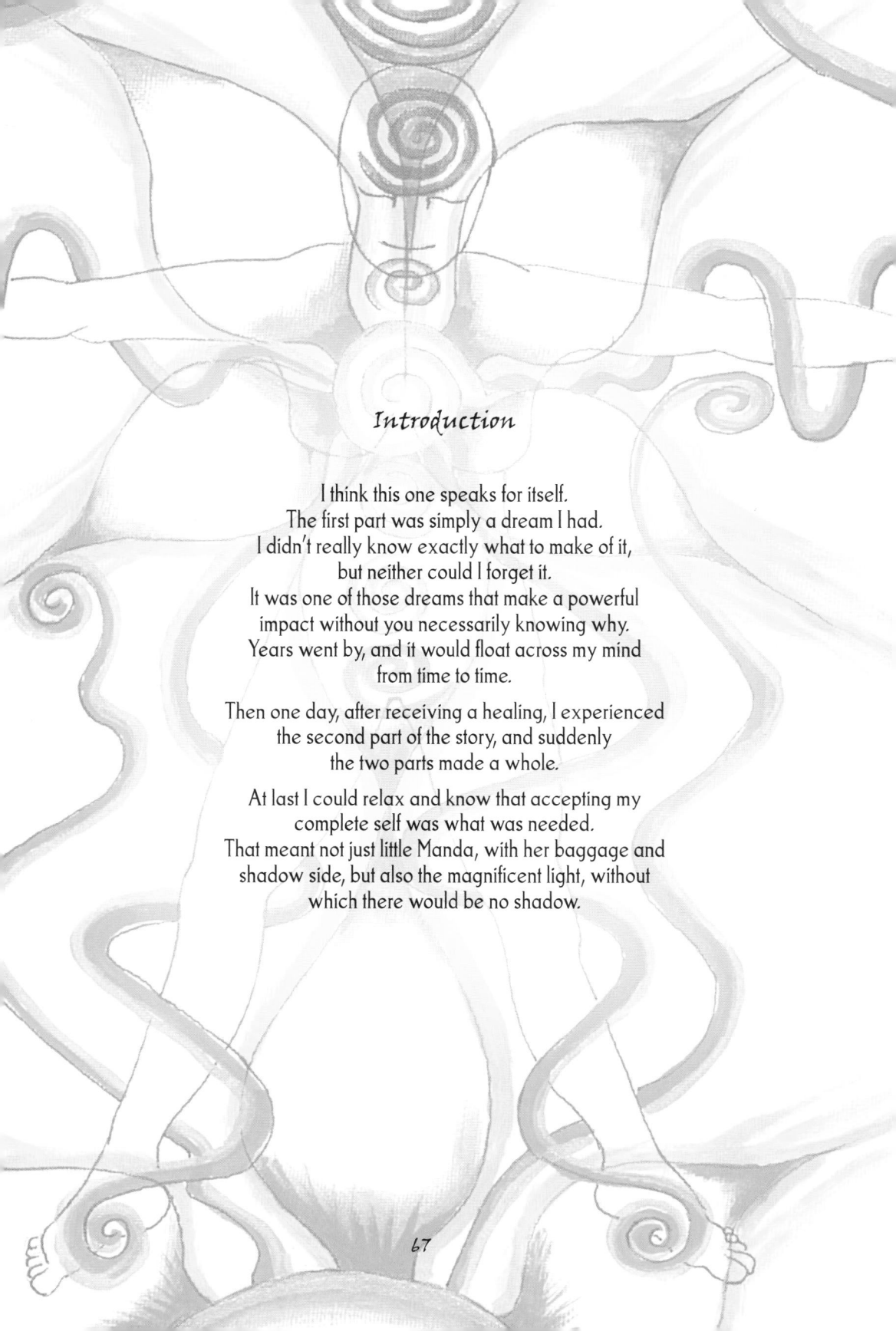

Introduction

I think this one speaks for itself.
The first part was simply a dream I had.
I didn't really know exactly what to make of it,
but neither could I forget it.
It was one of those dreams that make a powerful
impact without you necessarily knowing why.
Years went by, and it would float across my mind
from time to time.

Then one day, after receiving a healing, I experienced
the second part of the story, and suddenly
the two parts made a whole.

At last I could relax and know that accepting my
complete self was what was needed.
That meant not just little Manda, with her baggage and
shadow side, but also the magnificent light, without
which there would be no shadow.

Awoman had a dream. In her dream, she was being called to a particular place. When she arrived, many people were gathered. As she moved amongst the many, she realised that what had, at first, seemed like a chaotic crowd at one end of the room was, at the other, being meticulously sorted.

As she moved nearer the point of organisation, she noticed some people being sent one way, others another. When her turn came, she saw that the two people separating and ordering the crowd were two people she recognised.

They had helped her many times, when the madness of life had made her sick. The test they were using to determine which was your route was if, or how, you could put a chopstick down a Guppy's throat. The test seemed strange and made no sense except that it fitted in to the general feel of the day - just one more strange twist in a day full of the unexpected.

The woman held the little fish and slid the chopstick down its throat. Following this, she was ushered in through the left hand door. When she got into this room, she was amongst many women.

None of the women seemed to know why they were here or what happened next. Different women reacted in different ways to the situation they found themselves in. Many, like her, the woman noticed, had surrendered themselves to the strangeness of the situation and stood, with resignation in their eyes, like rounded up cattle.

Eventually, the woman saw her two tester friends enter, shut the door behind them and pick their way through the crowd, then mount a dais.

They explained that soon the world would be under attack. The attackers were not cruel on purpose, but many would get hurt. They told the crowd of the universal playboys and girls who travelled the cosmos, looking for ways to amuse themselves. These God-like beings were coming into our neck of the woods to play in the Earth's playground, like spoilt children with their toys. Their incredible powers would be used to dazzle and seduce. They would take no responsibility for their meddling and would leave when bored, moving to the next place and the newest games for their enjoyment. Behind them, they would leave chaos and confusion.

But in preparation, seeds had been planted in the human stock. Prophecies told how these human seedlings would awaken at the time of need to be guardians of the Earth.

"So, welcome seedlings, I'm here to awaken you. The time is now: your special powers will be your goodness and virtue. your ordinariness is what will save the Earth and restore balance."

The women looked around at each other, not yet being able to take in what had been imparted. Some felt sure it was a joke, others felt they may have accidentally walked into the wrong room. Some felt absolutely nothing, having reached weirdness overload - they had shut down and now the events of the day washed over them.

But others felt a strange stirring, a feeling they were sure had not been there before. A distant memory seemed to be struggling to find its way to consciousness.

The two speakers climbed from the stage and walked towards the door through which they had come. The women stopped them.

"Aren't you coming with us?"

"No," they replied, "We are not part of your group. Our job was to get you here, now it's up to you."

The woman felt abandoned as she watched them leave and, with them, her anchor. Now she was all at sea. Then, the great doors at the end of the room were pushed open, and gradually the hustling, bustling crowd passed through in a mighty wave.

But there were some who felt a strange stirring. A feeling they were sure had not been there before

She stood blinking in the sunlight on the pavement. Like a cinema crowd, let out by the side door, they were now straight onto the street.

The woman looked around. Some of her previous companions stood like her, confused, wondering what had happened. Others started to move away, disappearing into the life on the street.

Eventually, the woman realised that she had been dismissed. She looked around, trying to fathom what to do next.

She saw a bus stop and joined the waiting line. The bus came. She sat upstairs. Here, she could view this ordinary street on what was, for most, an ordinary day.

"So." she thought, "I'm here to save the Earth." But it sounded ridiculous, dramatic and unreal. Her mind couldn't quite grasp the meaning of the strange events of the day.

"How can we fight with our ordinariness?" Her thoughts ran through the catalogue of superheroes she, and the rest of her culture, had been brought up on. Not even a pair of tights or a cape had she or her fellow freedom fighters.

She looked at the passers-by on the street below. "I'm here to save you," she thought, "but what do you see? Just a woman on a bus."

The woman woke from her dream. She felt both thrilled to be doing such important work, and at the same time, unimpressed with her sense of unimportance.

The months and years rolled by. The woman concentrated on being ordinary. She worked, she watched TV, she cooked roast dinner on Sundays, she cried, she laughed, and she wondered exactly how this was helping.

Meanwhile, her love of the Earth grew full and round. The more she lived and learned and realised, the more she became confused. This ordinariness seemed to be choking her. She knew that she couldn't save the world, but she also doubted her ability to save herself.

Then gradually, the princess awakened, after many years of nightmares and dreams. She saw that it had all been a sleeping illusion - dreams within dreams. She now saw what a magnificent being of light she, and those around her, were.

She blinked her eyes to accustom herself to the vital brilliance she saw in every living thing. So long had she been slumbering, she needed time to adjust to the fullness of beauty that now met her senses. She shut her eyes again:

"Which is the dream - which is the wakening?"

This time, as she opened her eyes, she knew for sure. She could now remember back before the time of her sleeping and the periods of wakefulness between times. As she looked around, she recognised a few of the people she saw, but now, uncloaked, they looked different. Each shone in their own way; each sang their harmony to the song of the Universe.

The penny dropped. This was the ordinariness that she needed to embrace. The other was the madness of her slumbering. In the ordinariness of her magnificence, she finally understood how the Earth was being saved. How every person on this Earth was being guided through the same door as she had been in her dream.

She was more awake now, but still not fully. She saw the thicket of thorns that had grown up around her sleeping body. She knew she still had work to do - every thorn represented a misplaced thought, a constricting assumption about the meaning of her ordinariness. She

would enjoy her pruning, allowing light to fall where previously there had only been shade from the tangled branches.

She had been asleep, but now she was waking, and in her ordinariness, went to find her pruning saw.

After which, she went to start cooking Sunday dinner.

you are invited to affirm

So my brilliant, shining friend, let's get pruning.

Make a safe space.

Close your eyes and take a deep breath. See yourself uncloaked – big bright and beautiful. This is the real you. Keep turning up the brilliance of this picture.
Acknowledge that this is the true nature of all humanity – the rest is a dream.
Wake up now to accept how big and powerful you really are.
Look down and see the thicket of thorns that has grown around you whilst being asleep to this truth. Each thorn is a trap that keeps you ensnared
in the belief that you are small, powerless or inadequate.
You have a magic pair of secateurs to cut yourself free.
As you cut through the thicket, become aware of what these thorns represent.
What limiting thoughts are you holding and perpetuating in your thinking?
How do these thoughts limit you?
As you touch the thorns with your magic secateurs, you become aware of
how to turn these thoughts around so that you set yourself free to grow.
Each transformed way of thinking then becomes a rose. Breathe in the fragrance
of this bloom and let the new way of thinking and perceiving your life flower
inside you – if you want to know who you truly are, smell a rose.
Take a deep breath, taking the perfume into your whole body,
then open your eyes.
Turn your rose into a positive affirmation,
write it down and put it where you can read it as often as you need.
Imagine the perfume of the rose and let the fragrance set your heart free.
Keep going back 'til your thicket of thorns has all been transformed into a rose
garden. Then enjoy the garden and any occasional pruning that's needed to
maintain your magnificence.

A Note on Positive Affirmations

Always concentrate on the most desired outcome and then state it as if that
outcome was already realised e.g. if one of your thorns is "there is not enough time to
work with this exercise" then your positive affirmation would be:

*I have all the time I need right NOW to weed my inner garden and enjoy the
fragrance of the rose that I am.*

Grandmother Lakewater...

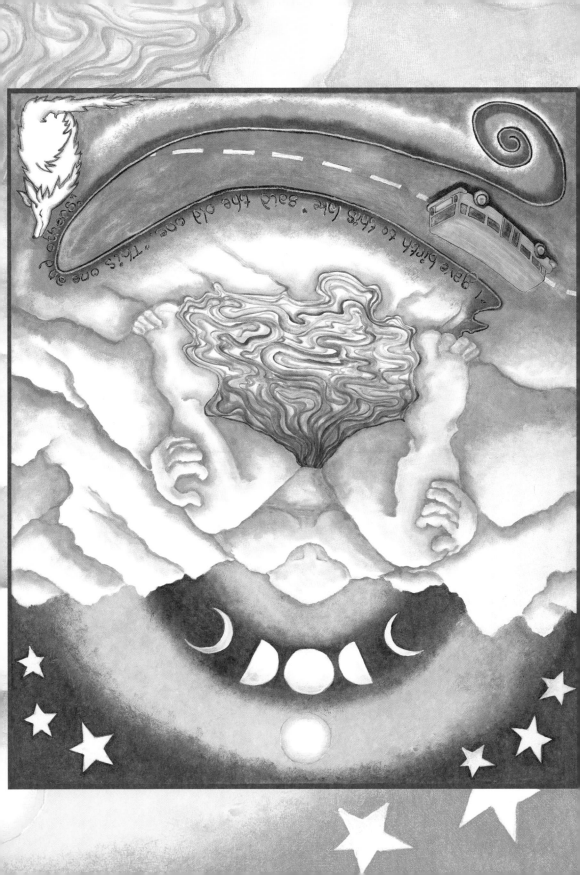

"I gave birth to this one," said the old one. "This one and others."

Introduction

Around the end of 2001 and the beginning of 2002, I became aware
of a group of energy beings I know by the name of "The Grandmothers".

I'd been courting their assistance for at least a year as I'd started a group for teenage girls.
The girls were twelve to thirteen years of age and confused about the
changes they were going through. I'd had no experience of being held in such a group
when I was a teenager and neither had I run this kind of "rites of passage" before,
even though I'd worked with teenagers. I needed help, so I called to the Grandmothers,
who knew how to be happy in this Earth walk and had held their maidens in circle
and seen them through the gateways of adolescence into adulthood.

I needed to be held, so that I could hold the girls. I felt the Grandmothers' presence and
followed my inspiration as to how to proceed. Today the girls are twenty two and
twenty three years old, and what an enormous privilege the journey has been.

But getting back to 2001, I went for a healing. The Grandmothers came and built a moonhut
within my belly. This was the start of a phase that was to last for the next two years.
The woman who'd given me the healing and I started to journey to the Grandmothers.
We were asked to work together running workshops,
creating circles of women who would then continue to hold the energy.

The first year's workshops were called "Entering the Moonhut" and those of the second
year, "Weaving the Web". I made many journeys during this time,
and four of them are amongst this collection.

In "A Woman Called Heavy Shoulders" I'd been shown how my
feelings of unworthiness were still holding me back. This old onion again!
How many layers was I going to have to keep peeling off
before I got to the original point at which this had become an issue?

This inspired the question I asked before making the Grandmother Lakewater journey.
We were in one of the "Entering the Moonhut" circles and I found myself sitting
in the north-east of the circle. For me, the north-east is the dark place
just before the sun rises in the east, the place between death and re-birth
– the ideal place to let go, before starting again.

here was once a woman who, despite wanting to play her part in healing the Earth, knew that she had a problem with self-worth. No matter how much she wanted to give of herself in service, her lack of worth always told her it was not enough. She felt as if she was breaking her own heart, which of course she was.

So she set out on her journey to the Grandmothers' moonhut to ask for help and healing. To her dismay, she found herself accompanied by Coyote. She had met this coyote before - she was one of two sisters that had lived on her heavy, aching shoulders.

They had whispered to her quietly, telling her that she was lazy or stupid. They had suggested ways for her to make amends, but they had always resulted in her affirming just how lazy and stupid she was. They hadn't done it to be cruel; they had done it to illustrate what happens when you don't listen to your heart.

She had grown stronger from listening to the space between their whisperings and the wisdom of love. But there was still a vulnerability about the woman that she could not get to grips with. Why would she listen to the beating of the coyotes when she knew how to listen to her own heart? But listen she did, and sometimes, she still believed them.

And so you see why she was dismayed when, on that day, the day she wanted to heal her vulnerability, she found herself escorted by the trickster.

As she arrived at the moonhut, the Grandmothers inside were singing a particularly raucous version of the "One Heart" song. She was welcomed into the hut but coyote stayed outside.

The Grandmothers sitting in the north-east beckoned the woman to them. They laid her down, and as they did so, the rest of the circle receded back until they disappeared, along with their singing. Then the Grandmothers that remained

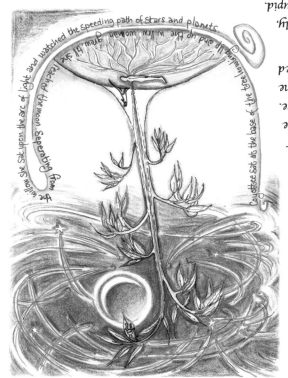

watched the speeding path of stars and planets

grew till she reached the moon and up and up the willow woman

Separating from the willow She sat upon the arc of light and

Coyote sat at the base of the trunk of the green willow tree

started to prepare the woman for a ritual death. She knew her healing would come about from the death of her distrust in herself. They buried her in the ground. She lay below, in the dark soil, surrendering herself to the healing the old woman offered.

Then she felt a shift in herself. Her energy started to shoot from the ground. She was a willow tree and was growing strong and fast. She grew and grew, until the moonhut peeled away and disappeared, taking the Grandmothers with it. Coyote sat at the base of the tree and howled. Up and up the willow woman grew, until she reached the moon.

There was a huge arc of light around the moon. It was on to this that she stepped, separating from the willow and taking up her woman form again. She sat upon the bow of light and watched the speeding path of stars and planets. It was as though she sat in the only still point of the Universe. Everything else moved so rapidly that it seemed nothing but blurs rushing past. Then, as suddenly as everything had sped up, time resumed its normal pace.

She looked at the willow and saw that it was starting to die and its journey towards death was taking it back to Earth. She merged back into the willow, and the energy that had thrust her into the sky now returned her back to her grave in the dark soil that the Grandmothers had buried her in.

The woman dug her way out of the grave, away from death's embrace and clear of the moonhut, which was now deserted. She walked through the woods until she came to a road. It was a large, empty highway, silent apart from the sound of an approaching vehicle. It was a turquoise bus, and as she watched it pass, she saw coyote sitting on the back seat staring back at her. For a short moment the woman watched as it drove on, leaving her alone on the road. Then, instantaneously, she knew she needed to be on that bus. She began to run, waving her hands and shouting. It stopped and she was able to board. Panting, she made her way down the central aisle and placed herself next to coyote on the back seat. Once the woman had caught her breath, she asked the coyote where they were going.

"I don't know," was the reply. "I was following you!"

The woman's blank face belied the confusion that tumbled around inside her head. She arose to ask the driver where they were headed.

"North-east," was all that he would reply.

The bus stopped in a bleak landscape and the woman and her companion alighted. The bus moved off, leaving her to contemplate her surroundings.

It was a barren place where steep, rocky inclines tumbled down to a lake. The lake must have been exceptionally deep and had the unnerving, otherworldly energy that very deep water can sometimes hold.

What secrets did its depth conceal? The woman noticed that no birds sang here. There was nothing to soften the feeling of crossing a threshold into another time or reality. It wasn't hostile, but nor was it comfortable.

The woman noticed an old lady making her way through the landscape towards them. She recognised her as one of the Grandmothers from the north-east, but strangely, she now appeared to be pregnant.

"Surely the old woman must be beyond child-bearing age?" thought the woman. But as the Grandmother came close enough for them to greet each other, the woman could see that indeed, she was swollen of belly.

It was not so much a warm meeting as one befitting the backdrop it took place against. The two women stood side by side and the younger felt the Grandmother's deep, mysterious energy. It was not hostile, just other-worldly. They both looked at the lake and, eventually, the woman asked the elder about it.

"I gave birth to this lake," replied the old one. "This one and others."

The woman looked at the old one, her belly, and the lake, and then remembered why she had set out. She asked the Grandmother about her problem with self-worth.

The old one guided the woman into the lake. She held her hand and knees as the woman birthed light into the water.

"You do not value yourself because you have been tricked out of recognising what you do," she was told.

Though she heard the words, they did not help. She couldn't remember a time when she had felt the self-worth she had been tricked out of.

"So what should I do?" she asked, hoping to reveal the meaning of the Grandmother's statement.

The old one turned to meet her gaze. The woman noticed the ancient eyes, holding the same mystery as the watery depths of the lake, but more than that, they also held the rocky valley that held the water. They held the aeons of time from the birthing of the lake and they held the knowledge the woman was seeking.

"You are a birther too," the old one said simply but emphatically. The woman automatically put her hands to her belly. She felt the rounded hump of her sacral centre and asked, "What do I birth?"

"The light," was the reply. This stark answer bowled over the woman. She had known this answer already - she had just never let herself completely own it. She had feared she might be deluding herself. It was too perfect, too beautiful, but it was what her heart ached to do.

The Grandmother took the woman by the shoulders. She was strong and gritty, like the place. She shook the woman. "Own it!" she demanded. The Grandmother was being forceful now; she offered no comfort, just the hard truth. "Own it!" she repeated.

The strongest barrier between the woman and the acknowledgement of her beauty was herself. She found it hard to acknowledge that much beauty, let alone own it, but the force of the old one broke her down. She cried, and her hard shell cracked. The truth of what the old one imparted seeped into her, like a deep lake of understanding.

The Grandmother softened at last. She could see that the message had hit home. She held the woman, allowing her to cry. She needed to cry in order to fill the lake forming inside of her; the belly waters of understanding.

When the woman's sobs had receded, the Grandmother explained further: "Because you have not acknowledged what you do with your belly, you have felt obligated to carry the work mantle on your shoulders. You've been trying to prove yourself worthy of the space you occupy, paying your way. But this is not your way. The wounds from the work yoke gave the coyote sisters a place to live. They have been whispering to you over many lifetimes."

The woman reached for her shoulders and placed her fingers on the scars. She rubbed them gently, easing out her neck and offering a tender touch to their soreness. She understood why she had no recollection of being worthy. It was such a long time ago that she had been tricked into believing the power of the womb was not of value, or worse, that it was the root of shame and sin.

But how had she been tricked out of seeing her own value? It didn't matter now, for she had come full circle.

The old one guided the woman into the lake; she held her hand and knee as the woman birthed light into the water.

"Together, we can create rainbows," the old one whispered, smiling at the woman.

She helped her back onto the shore and laid her down. Coyote joined them. The old lady acknowledged the dog with a knowing look and gestured with her head towards the woman's shoulders. The coyote sister licked at the wounds, licking out the pain and the dismissal of the woman's true worth, healing a whole cycle of mistrust in the power of the womb - for her and all the other women who had come before her. The woman felt guilty for the dismay she had felt upon seeing her coyote but she allowed this to be overshadowed by a deeper sense of gratitude and respect.

The Grandmother could see that her work was almost complete. She called out to her sisters and the moonhut reappeared. The circle of Grandmothers held the woman as a newly birthed mother. They sang the "One Heart" song to her

The coyote sister sucked at the wounds, licking out the pain. Licking out the dismissal of her true worth. Healing the woman's scars. Healing a whole cycle of mistrust in the power of the womb. Hers and all the women who'd come before her.

She sent them her silent blessings before turning to make her way home.

softly and gently. They rubbed her body and helped her to appreciate herself as a birther.

The woman knew she was fully restored when the sweet vibration started to bubble up into the hubbub of everyday life.

She sang for the old women, a funny song that she knew from her childhood. It created a sense of fun and mischief inside of her. She embraced all of the Grandmothers many times, especially Grandmother Lakewater. As she did so, she rubbed her belly against the others in thanks for the treasure she had been given.

Coyote was not around to see the woman home. The woman knew that the coyote sisters would find plenty of work to do in the world.

What do you birth?

Make a list of everything that has come
into the world because you created it.
What dreams have you made manifest?
What thoughts have you turned into actions?
What feelings have you given expression to?
What is now in the world because you made it so?

Then, make another list.

What do you want to give birth to in the future?
What thoughts need turning into actions?
What feelings want to be expressed?

You are the creator of your life.

How beautifully can you dream?
How fabulously can you think?
How courageously can you feel?

Rub your belly, acknowledge the birther you are.
Now have a cup of tea and a piece of toast to
celebrate that which you have already created.

Truth and Beauty...

Tiny threads, millions of them, shimmering living light connecting to the light web

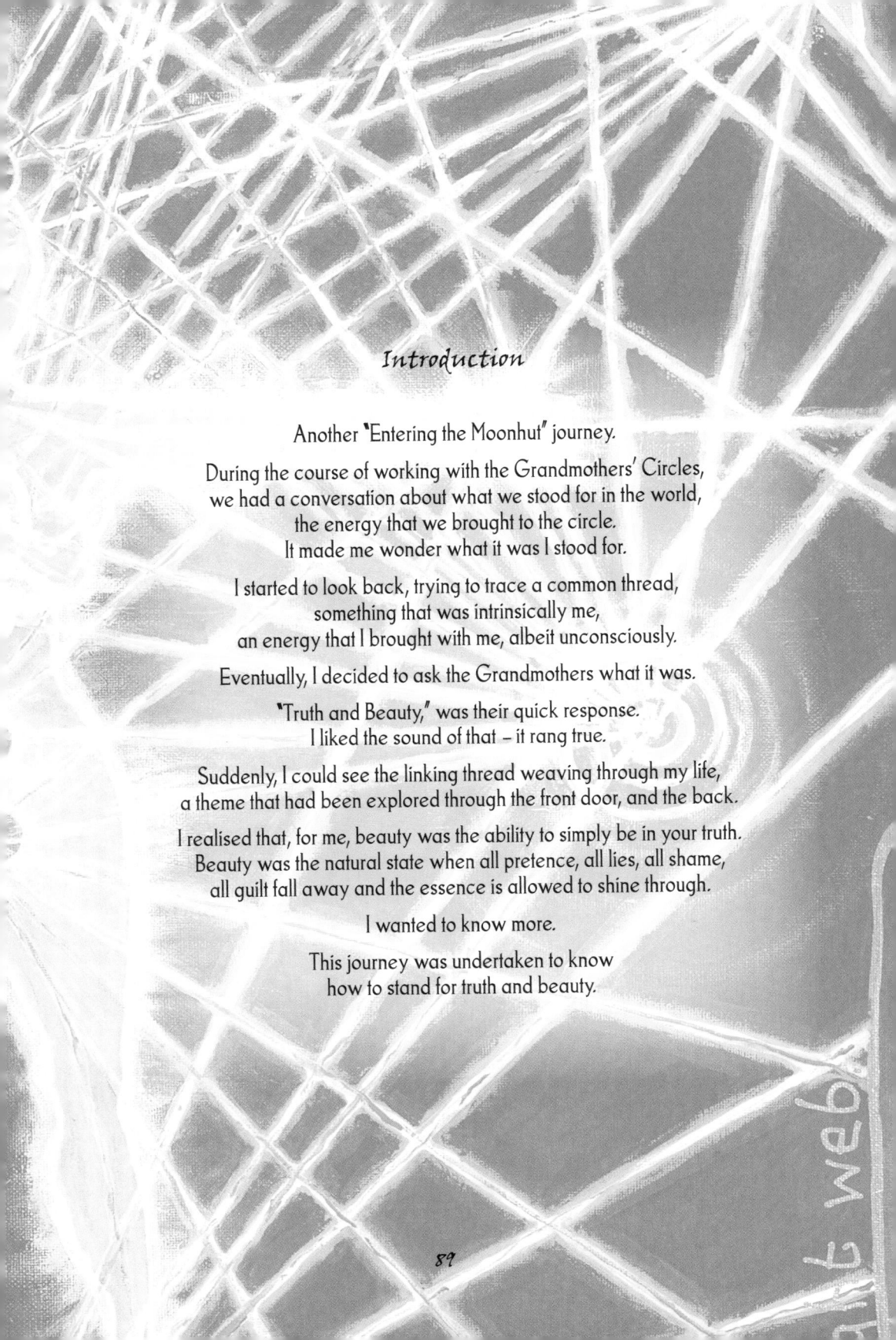

Introduction

Another "Entering the Moonhut" journey.

During the course of working with the Grandmothers' Circles,
we had a conversation about what we stood for in the world,
the energy that we brought to the circle.
It made me wonder what it was I stood for.

I started to look back, trying to trace a common thread,
something that was intrinsically me,
an energy that I brought with me, albeit unconsciously.

Eventually, I decided to ask the Grandmothers what it was.

"Truth and Beauty," was their quick response.
I liked the sound of that – it rang true.

Suddenly, I could see the linking thread weaving through my life,
a theme that had been explored through the front door, and the back.

I realised that, for me, beauty was the ability to simply be in your truth.
Beauty was the natural state when all pretence, all lies, all shame,
all guilt fall away and the essence is allowed to shine through.

I wanted to know more.

This journey was undertaken to know
how to stand for truth and beauty.

As the egg nourished her she realised that this was the egg of truth

*T*here was once a woman who needed to know how to stand for truth and beauty. From this place, she needed to know how to acknowledge the truth and beauty of every living thing. But she needed help. To this end, she went to visit the wise women who live in the trees.

After asking for permission, she entered the moonhut. The Grandmothers' hut was constructed of wood, woven together from the forest it sat in. Inside sat a circle of ten crones, and together they held an abundance of wisdom which weaved through and between them. This wisdom they offered to those who came and asked respectfully.

The woman was guided to the back of the lodge. She sat in the circle with the old ones who stared into the One Heart fire. The woman ignored the flames, and instead, studied the faces of the ancient ones that made up this circle. They were hard to see in the dim light of the lodge, but as the light of the fire danced across them, the woman saw faces that had experienced life and learned to believe in love above all else.

She was beckoned forward and asked to state her reason for the visit. It was then that the woman noticed an enormous egg in the fire. She was told to climb into the flame and hatch it.

She waded through the flames and clambered onto the egg. She had only been there seconds before she found herself inside it. Inside the smooth, oval shell, all other realities disappeared. Gone was the lodge, gone were the Grandmothers and gone was her ordinary life with her husband and children.

The yolk of the egg was feeding her right into her belly button. As it nourished her, she realised that this was the egg of truth. It was the egg that the circle of Grandmothers held within their centre.

The woman didn't know how long she lay in the egg absorbing the truth, but a point came when the yolk was spent and she filled the space. It was at this point that she cracked through the shell and found herself hatched into the embers of the fire.

The Grandmothers gathered around her. They rubbed ash from the fire all over her body. When they had finished, and the whole of her was deep grey and smelling of wood smoke, she was told it was time for her to leave.

Leaving the moonhut was much like hatching from the shell. Her world expanded again - she blinked at the light and saw everything fresh and new. She felt the push to move on, but knew not where to go.

She walked into the trees until she came upon a clearing. She lay down on the wet grass. It was raining - warm, growing rain. It gently washed away the grime of her birthing, but more than this, she felt as though the rain reached deep inside her making her sparkly on the inside: sparkly like the droplets of water hanging as jewels from the blades of grass surrounding her. As she rolled around in the grass, she heard a little of the truth she had absorbed bubble up into her consciousness:

"The truth is buried deep to protect it, not to hide it."

As the rain continued to penetrate the woman, she felt her belly swell like a rehydrating seed. She knew she was going to give birth to the truth baby.

The child came pushing its way out of her body. The woman held it in her arms. The placenta was still inside her. She held the baby against the backdrop of the sky, threw back her head, opened her mouth wide and swallowed the baby. As the placenta came away from her womb, she swallowed that also.

She felt like she had awoken from a strange and disturbing dream, and as she realised what she had done, a wave of anxiety swept through her. She called out through the rain to the Grandmothers and cried as she sat in the wet grass, feeling alone and in need of reassurance. But the Grandmothers didn't come. They sat in their circle and held her in trust.

Maybe the woman felt it, because there, in the wet grass, she started to feel not alone but that she just needed to trust herself. She could feel herself ingesting the truth. As her body absorbed it, it began to ooze out of her skin as a sticky substance.

She got up and walked, rubbing herself on the beings that she met - rocks, plants and trees. As she rubbed her sticky ooze onto a tree, it said to her,

"I feel the truth of who you are." She pulled back, staring at the trunk.

Then she fell into an embrace with the tree - how good it felt to know that this being felt the truth of her! What a relief to know that she could not hide or lie!

"Show me how to walk in truth and beauty," she asked the tree.

"I can only show you how to stand in it. You need to stand in it for now - walking is for later," the tree replied.

The woman sat in the tree but she couldn't get comfortable. Something just wasn't right. Then, she realised what it was:

"I need to be in your hidden aspect, in your roots. They will teach me the first thing I need to really know about how to stand in truth and beauty."

She held the baby against the backdrop of the sky.

The tree agreed, and so the woman went down into the system of roots that held the tree, allowing it to stand through wind, rain or shine, frost or drought.

She lay in the darkness, feeling the movement of energy. The roots spoke to her and told her how they held structure, but by doing so, they also defined the void - the spaces between. As if this was an invitation, the woman dived into the held space and spun into the void. What happened there can only be read about between these lines for words cannot define it.

Eventually, the woman found herself in another part of the root system. As she climbed upon the structure of this solid place, she realised that something of the energy she had experienced in the void she now carried in her own heart. So she dived into her heart and found it was huge. She realised her own heart had been the doorway to the One Heart. This vast place, filled with all the love of the Universe, held her in its nothingness.

She sang songs of love and light for the Earth. Her singing filled her and emptied her, both at the same time. As she sang, she knew that it was time to declare herself for what she stood for in the world.

As she did so, she felt a great "yes!" resounding through the One Heart. She stood strong, well rooted like a tree, arms reaching out. She felt threads of light shooting both through and from her body. Tiny threads, millions of them, shimmering, living light, connected her to the light web.

She continued to sing as the light pulsed through her, sewing her into the beautiful embroidery of light that wove around the planet and beyond, out into the Universe. The speeding light seemed to obliterate any notion of a physical body. All else but the myriad of shimmering threads receded, until all that was left was light and the darkness it defined by its absence.

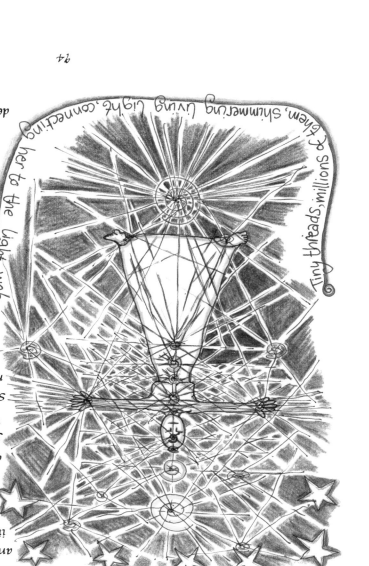

Tiny threads, millions of them, shimmering living Light, connecting her to the Light web

She had found her power spot and was experiencing what it felt like to be connected, plugged in, powerful. No one else could stand in her spot, only her. If she didn't do it, then the opportunity to ground some of this light was missed.

She thought how the world might be if every sacred being was standing in their spot.

As she stood in her spot, the beauty of the Earth flowered before her eyes, revealing wonders beyond measure. She became aware of the many beings who were already working consciously with the light grids. She knew that, one day, every human being would be called upon to declare what they stood for.

"Wow!" she thought, and what more could she think?

She sang Grandmother Truth's song:

The seeds of truth, they grow and grow,
in me, in you.
It's time to sow the seeds of truth,
they grow and grow,
through me, through you,
from long ago.

She found the song taking her back to the moonhut and to the Grandmothers who hold the egg of truth in their centre.

They welcomed her back, placing her in the middle of their circle, asking her to declare herself.

The woman allowed her feet to find her spot. She expanded her chest to reveal her open heart. She threw her arms open and held her head high.

"I stand for truth and beauty," she bellowed into the circle. The old ones clapped and whooped. They celebrated the woman's declaration by stomping their feet and singing raucously.

When the time came for the woman to leave, the Grandmothers were still celebrating noisily. The woman bid them farewell, but slipped out quietly, not wanting to break up the party. As she walked away, back down the path, she felt the joy of their singing, as it permeated through the wood, until she turned a corner and could hear them no more. Then all that she was left with was the gentle singing of her own heart, which guided her home.

you are invited to stand

Make a safe space to be for the next half hour or so.
Turn off the phone; make sure you won't be disturbed.

Sit or lie comfortably. Close your eyes and breathe in the sweet breath of life.
Exhale and release anything that distorts your truth and beauty.
Remember, your beauty is your ability to express your true nature.
A daffodil expresses itself as a daffodil, a stone as a stone
and a dog as a dog. Who are you really? See a path in front of you.
Notice everything you can about this path. What is it made from? What's either side?
What time of day is it? What season? Is it straight? Or does it curve?

Keep following the path. Notice any changes. Notice how you feel. The path is leading
you to a special place. It's a place only you can go. It's the centre of your universe.

You are nearly there, just a little further to go. In the next three steps, you will be there.
So, take one step, then another. Then, before the next step, just stop for a moment.
Breathe in deeply, then exhale. Take the next step and arrive in your power spot.

Feel yourself plug into the Earth and feel the rhythms of the Mother taking your root.
The top of your head is connected to the heavens. Feel your star nature expanding your
perceptions. By plugging in, you activate this spot – by standing as a Heavenly Earth
Star person, you create a marriage of Heaven and Earth. Feel the lovers' union as they
connect within your body. From your truth and beauty, ask what you stand for.
What particular quality of energy do you bring to the great circle of life?
Take a moment of quiet to perceive your truth.

Thank the great weave of the Universe for showing you the thread you are.
You are the gift. You give it every time you align with your power spot. The energy that
descends through the layers of your being into physical form has a clear runway each
time you stand centred. No one else can light this particular spot, only you. Without
you doing so, it remains unlit. You have stood here before. Maybe when gardening
or meditating or listening to music, laughing or watching a sunset or whilst peeling
carrots. It's the place where, just for a moment, everything makes sense and you realise
you only ever need to be yourself. Your true nature is when everything you think you
should be is stripped away. You are powerful when you let your true beauty shine.

Breathe deeply, feeling the full connection within yourself, then open your eyes.
If you didn't get a clear answer, notice how it comes to you over the next few days.

Take delight in knowing that you are enough, you have enough and you do enough.
Your power spot is you. You take it wherever you go.
Wherever you are, you can bring your light.

How great is that!

There was once a woman
who had a seal
as a teacher and a friend...

Some were cold. Some were still and some moved in mighty heaves... to many different parts of the woman as the ocean did.

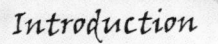

Introduction

This story was from a catch-up journey to a valued friend.
It was a journey into the teachings of the South
direction of the medicine wheel.

At this time, I was working with the Lakota wheel in which
South is the element of water and the place of the child,
the place to trust feelings and intuitions.

Whilst I have much power in this direction, I also have wounds.
This journey was undertaken to empower the South wisdom and
became a gentle reminder that all my feelings are valued teachers;
also, that I must own my feelings but not let them own me.
Some feelings are warm, some are challenging, some are lonesome
and others are sociable. They come and go and leave their mark.

At the time of making this journey, I still needed to actively remind
myself that all my feelings were good feelings, in as much as they all
spoke to me of where I was in relationship with my soul's wishes.

The wisdom of the child is to play
– that's what I needed more of in my life –
and Seal was the perfect playmate.

*T*here was once a woman who had a seal as a teacher and friend. The woman hadn't visited Seal in some while and she missed her. She decided to pay her a visit and ask her how to sit in the summer of her life.

When she arrived at the beach, the summer sunshine sparkled on the water. The blueness of the sky reflected turquoise in the sea. She walked across the empty beach watching the footprints she left in the pristine sands. Her mind stretched across the time from when these grains had been rock. Now, the fine grains sifted through her toes.

A seagull flew overhead and brought her back from her mind's wandering.

The woman reached the water's frothing edge. She stood, witnessing the water rush at her feet, then retreat ready to rush again. She felt the sea steal the very sand she stood upon with every rushing wave.

Then, slowly, she entered the cold wetness. Each wave claimed new heights on her body until, eventually, she surrendered to them. Now she dived into the waves, enjoying the embrace of tide and current pulling her body further into its energetic dance.

Suddenly Seal was there. Without need for invitation, the two friends played in the surf.

As they made their way back to the beach, the woman asked Seal her question.

Seal told the woman to dig a hole in the sand; this the woman did.

She scooped wet sand out, feeling the gritty grains under her nails. Now the sand was everywhere. Every now and then, she felt the gritty crunch between her teeth, showing that even her insides were not safe from the sand's reach.

The woman reached the nothing edge. She stood allowing the water to rush at her feet, then retreat, ready to rush again.

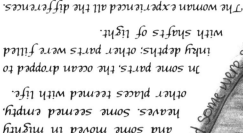

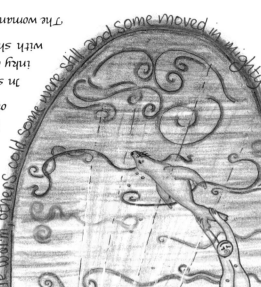

102

Once she had completed her task, she looked up to see her friend watching. Seal admired her work - "It's an excellent hole, now fill it with water."

The woman returned to the sea. With cupped hands, she took some of the ocean to the hole in the sand. Each time the water either slipped through her fingers, or that which reached its destination was seen to quickly disappear and make its way back to the sea.

The woman tried to fill the hole many times. She enjoyed watching the water fill the bottom of the hole and then disappear.

Each time, the hole got smaller as the water took the sand with it, only to leave it at the bottom. She scooped out the soggy bottom, patting it back to the sides and made good the top edge. Then back to the sea.

She placed her hands for the coming wave to wash the sand from them, then another scoop of water. Eventually, smiling, the woman looked up to see her friend warming her body in the sun.

"It can't be done." declared the woman.

""No." said the seal. "Imagine the sand is you and the water your emotions. The sand knows how to be in good relation with the water - it allows the water to move through it, to feel it, without holding on."

The woman was hot from her toil so the two friends returned to the water. Seal took the woman to many different parts of the ocean. Some were warm, others cold. Some were still and some moved in mighty heaves. Some seemed empty, other places teemed with life. In some parts, the ocean dropped to inky depths; other parts were filled with shafts of light. The woman experienced all the differences.

She noticed which ones comforted her and which ones challenged. The ones that soothed her and the ones that called to the Warrior. Eventually, they came to the rocks at the side of the beach and Seal showed her a game of falling off the rocks into the water.

"The sea will catch you," Seal reassured the woman, as if it were some kind of trust game. The more the woman jumped, the more reassured she became about the waiting arms of the ocean.

Tired now, the two friends flopped down onto the beach. They warmed and dried themselves in the sunshine as their heart beats and breathing resumed their normal rates.

The woman asked her friend to teach her a dance. Seal showed her how to spiral in the water, first one way then the other. The woman tried, but the seal was a master of this dance. The woman shut her eyes and felt her dance spiralling from a place deep within.

"This feels great!" she exclaimed, "What is this dance?"

"It is the dance of purification," her friend told her.

The woman's eyes opened; her dancing stopped. The woman was not sure of her friend's answer. She sat at the meeting place of sea and shore and closed her eyes to meditate on the dance - to see if she could find her own answers to its name and qualities.

She composed herself, stilled her mind and opened herself up to receive what would come.

What came was a face full of sea water. She opened her eyes, after wiping the salty water from her face. She was just in time to see her friend make ready to send the next splash her way.

Seal laughed and teased the woman for the pomposity of her serious posturing. She

The two of them lay half in and half out of the water. Each salty rush tickled them with its frothy fingers. "Remember," said the Seal, "let life tickle you at every opportunity."

splashed until the woman had no choice but to join in her game.

"Remember," said Seal, "let life tickle you at every opportunity."

The two of them lay half in and half out of the water, each salty rush tickled them with its frothy fingers.

The woman broke from the deliciousness of the tickling to ask more questions of her teacher. But Seal told her to enjoy the moment - the water, the sand, the sea, the company and the good feeling they shared.

Seal looked at the sun and said, "To be light, don't carry your emotions with you. Water can be very heavy. Dive into them, explore them, feel them, then come to the shore and leave them behind. You are not your emotions."

The woman asked how she could embody this in her life.

"Most of all, having fun lightens you. Don't take yourself too seriously. Joy is a serious business."

The woman knew it was soon going to be time to leave. She looked at the seal.

"How can I say thank you to you, my friend?"

"Keep my home, the sea, clean, and always say Hello to my sisters."

Every good day needs to end and the woman had her own home to return to. She placed her arms around her beautiful teacher and felt the tickle of the seal's whiskers.

Then she left, giggling to herself as she allowed her memories to tickle her all the way home.

Every single emotion you have is telling you something you need to know. They are your teachers. Each one teaches you how to be with yourself. There are some teachers that are letting you know you have gone off track – they are there to guide you back. If you suppress them, you don't gain their wisdom. Some are confirming or lighting the way.

The track, or path, we are talking about is the instruction our higher selves give us to align our physical life to our soul.

Some of these emotions are uncomfortable to live with – anger, fear, jealousy, insecurity, frustration etc. But their message is to show you how to move through and back into the affirming emotions of joy, excitement, or the highest of all, love. All these emotions are in a relationship with love. Love is 'queen' of the emotions – she rules.
Not one of these difficult feelings is outside of her domain.
They are sent from your higher self to help you be in love with yourself.

Take a pen and a piece of paper and write down whichever uncomfortable emotion seems most pressing in your life at the moment.

(Note: depression is NOT an emotion but the act of suppressing emotions such as anger)

Hold the thought in your head that this feeling is lovingly sent to you, to guide you out of a wrong turning and to get you back on track.

Put your feet flat on the floor and visualise your root going down. Now direct your attention to the top of your head and visualise a line of energy connecting you to the guidance of your higher self. Ask for help in understanding what your soul is communicating to you through this emotion, then write down what this feeling is teaching you about love.

Read back what you have written and ask that any further insights you need will come in a way you can understand. Notice, over the next few days, any deeper understanding of what action you need to take to move back on track.
Let the 'queen' of emotions guide you. Keep going until you get the confirming emotions: excitement, peace, etc. and let them lead the way.

Instead of being irritated by these emotions, and trying to push them away, take the time to really listen. When you really listen to anger, you are listening to your own heart. When you really listen to fear, again, it is love that speaks to you. Hear its call to make changes either in your habitual thoughts or in your actions. Love is in all of your feelings, but in its most pure form, you will feel great. Don't be uncomfortable any longer than you need to be – move. Be responsible for yourself; give yourself the gift of being able to respond to the journey of life in the most loving way you can. Don't ignore the truth, however painful; at its core, it is a calling from your own heart to be true to yourself.

There was once a woman
who felt that not all was
right in the relationship
between men and women...

Introduction

My family moved in to our new home, which we hoped to turn into a healing space by running workshops and being more tuned in to the spirit of the land. This next story comes from a weekend in which we invited various friends to share the space with us.

We met as one group on the Friday night.
On the Saturday and Sunday morning the women journeyed together in their moonhut, and the men gathered and shared in the sun lodge.

The plan was that by Sunday afternoon, we would perform a blessing on each other: the men blessing the women and the women blessing the men. I was really looking forward to the weekend, and when I saw the astrological chart for this period, I felt assured that I'd been inspired in my choice of date as there was a real sun/moon thing going on at that time.

However, the chart showed that somehow
the moon was having a look at its male aspect and the sun at its femaleness.
This is exactly what happened.
The men spent their time crying and nurturing and healing each other
whilst the women landed up coping with conflict and aggression.
I spent a very large part of the weekend crying.
But by Sunday lunch time, the tears had carved a space inside me where
a deep sense of reverence for all life could sit, and most particularly,
an appreciation of my maleness and of men and the burdens they carry for the tribe.

The blessings we were then able to give and receive came from a place of authenticity.

I remember the men came to sing to us, to encourage us out of the moonhut.
They kept their distance and sang us "You Are My Sunshine" in a really sweet way.
Meanwhile, the women in the lodge felt bashful and shy of being seen by the men, even though these were friends, boyfriends and lovers. There was a nervousness, a sweet shyness, a vulnerability and with it, a hope of a new way of relating – both within the two aspects of self and within the relationships of male and female within the world.

The story is the culmination of my weekend.
I haven't included anyone else's experience as that is not my story to tell.

*T*here was once a woman who felt that not all was right in the relationship between men and women. She felt it in the two aspects that made her whole. She felt it in the relationships with the men she loved and she saw it in the world beyond her world. But what could she do? What healing or wisdom could she offer?

She was pondering this question when she went to visit Grandmother Juniper. The old woman was magical, and it was no accident that the woman found herself, at this time, in her presence.

As if reading her mind, Grandmother beckoned the woman up into the branches of a huge tree that grew nearby. Although the woman was preoccupied, she allowed herself to be encouraged further and further into the tree until, before she knew it, the old one was sitting in the furthest branches, gesturing for the woman to follow.

The woman had to let go of her wandering mind and become fully present. In this way, she was able to join the old one who whispered to her. "Feel alive, be light!"

Then the wind came, a gentle breeze at first, inviting them to dance.

The woman let go of her heaviness. She became so light that the wind could blow them both into its dancing embrace. It swirled and twirled them. When finally the wind placed its two dancing partners back upon the earth, they realised that they had become two little tree seeds. No sooner had they started to get a breath, a giant of a man (or so he seemed to them) came and plucked them from the ground and planted them into the moist earth.

They sat in the darkness and giggled. Everything tickled them because they were so light. Then amidst the giggling, something began to happen. Tickled by the damp, dark

"Feel alive, be light." Then a gentle wind came, a breeze at first, inviting them to dance.

soil, the two seeds began to split open and sprout. As sprouts they were able to dance in the sunshine. Here, above the soil, where their sprouting heads poked, the air was filled with golden sparkles, charging the atmosphere with glorious life.

The women rose from the earth, to dance in the shimmering light. It made them feel wild, exhilarated and daring. As they danced their wild dance, they held each other's hands and spun themselves round and round. Faster and faster they went until they entered the vortex of their intention, and off they rode to Venus.

When they got there, the tickling had stopped. Instead, a calm fell into the deep places inside of them. They found a lake in which to bathe, washing away the intoxicating excitement and immersing themselves in this new, different energy.

Beautiful women lined the shore, as they climbed out of the water. The two travellers recognised the serene beauty of this place, pulsating through the waiting daughters of this planet.

The woman remembered the question she had set out with that day. The daughters listened, but said nothing. Instead, they took the women to a place where a taut, red line of energy emerged from the planet, rising out and beyond. This line, the daughters told them, ended on Mars.

The Venusian women beckoned to a huge black bird. It carried, not an olive branch in its beak, but a whole young, slender tree. They asked the two visitors if they would ride the bird to Mars, taking this gift to the men there.

They explained that the tree was for the men to plant. This single tree would quickly become a whole forest. It would be a place of healing for the warriors to find solace, a place that would offer them comfort and nurture. A place to be quiet, to find peace in their hearts and wisdom for their future plans. A place to be vulnerable and, in so doing, find their strength.

The tree held the beautiful, serene energy of this place. The two women felt the love and respect these daughters offered to the sons of Mars.

They mounted the bird, and without need of words, bid farewell. The bird began to fly along the taut, red line.

But the further away from the planet they travelled, the more the calm serenity ebbed away, until all they were left with was a mounting sense of fear.

They felt unworthy of the trust placed upon them: every fibre of their being screamed to go no further. They told the bird of their predicament. The bird stopped to give them time. They called down the taut red line and asked to be met here, half way.

They waited, not sure what to expect. Before long, a son of Mars came flying towards them.

They greeted each other shyly, but respectfully. They noticed his noble stance and kindly, intelligent eyes. The women gave the tree and explained its nature. Then the man gave a gift to the women. It was a handful of broken arrows. With this gift came a request: that these broken relics of war be made into something new.

They thanked each other for their gifts and wished each other Godspeed. The man bowed before setting off the way he'd come. The women remounted the bird and also flew back.

The daughters of Venus told them that the arrows would be mended and charmed so that they would only be able to kill that which killed love. The two women were now keen to return to Earth. Holding hands, they travelled back the way they had come.

As the time came for the two women to part company, the woman felt that she'd been shown something important that she needed to embrace. She decided that she would like to plant up some little Oak trees from the two-leafers that were growing from last autumn's acorn fall.

She would find twelve men to whom they needed to be given. They would hold the essence of the forest in which they could find healing and solace. She'd been the tree seed. She knew the journey the acorn made: leaving the mighty Oak, splitting, being vulnerable, in order for new life to grow. She would know twelve men who needed to be tickled and showered in golden sparkles, to be bathed in serenity and blessed for their journey.

After planting up the young trees, the woman realised that, maybe, one of them should be for herself, to honour her inner male. Already, she had journeyed out to the furthest reaches of the tree and then beyond, into the cosmos.

They mounted the bird and began to fly along the taut red line.

Now, she realised, she needed to pull in. Every journey started from the depth of herself and she needed to back-track.

She looked at herself in the three mirrors of her dressing table. She saw herself going back further and further, repeating and repeating back into infinity. Each of her faces had two eyes which she found herself falling into, journeying down their dark tunnels until she fell through the mirror and, in doing so, split into her male and female aspects.

The two selves faced each other: between them, they held a rainbow ribbon. Still looking into each other's eyes, they stepped away from each other. As the gulf between them widened, the rainbow ribbon bridge, linking the two, became bigger, expanding, to fill the divide.

Back and back they stepped. So intent were they upon staring at each other, and the ever widening gap between them, that they didn't notice that they were starting to encircle the globe with their rainbow.

Although they didn't see it, they were now backing towards each other. It was quite a shock, when they again met, reversing right into each other.

Now the whole planet was wrapped in the rainbow of their parting. They looked at the beautiful encircling gift that they had made between them, even if they weren't quite sure exactly how it had come about. The male then spiralled up to the North Pole, whilst the female spiralled down to the South Pole. They felt the pull of attraction through the central axis, and suddenly, the woman was whole again - male and female united in one body.

The woman then, for the first time, got down on her hands and knees so that she could really examine the fabric of the rainbow bridge. As she got closer, she realised what it was made from. It was woven from all of the tears of sorrow and joy that came from living in physical bodies. The more she looked, the more amazed she became at the beauty woven from all human struggle: all the hopes and fears, every tear that had ever been shed, lit by the light of spirit, splitting each prism into rainbows of experience.

The wisdom keepers of the Earth then came. They took the woman off the rainbow bridge. Without saying a word, they drew the symbol for female, ♀ and then male, ♂ in the earth.

The woman looked at the male symbol, the circle with the arrow shooting from it. Waves of feeling penetrated deep into the woman, bringing her to her knees in the dirt. She had seen this symbol many times before, but now she felt it. Deep inside, an appreciation of its rich meaning unfolded, conveying itself to every cell of her body. A new understanding blossomed in her chest, ripping at her heart, tearing it open.

She saw the fall from grace, the loss of her inner noble warrior with its connection to all that is male. She had to face the truth. To survive on this physical planet, she had lived off the death of other sacred beings. The food she ate, her shelter, her transport: the maintenance of life at its most basic meant things died so she lived.

The woman lay in the dirt, having to fully face the truth. It wasn't just the deaths, it was also the refusal to fully acknowledge them: the lies she allowed herself, the shielding she wore to block out the reality. The female gave birth and the male maintained this new life. Her inner warrior was battered and bruised from the struggle to feed the ever-hungry lie. The cost was immense.

Her inner male knew the value of life, the journey that had to be made from the void, bringing the un-manifest across the bridge into this world. But in knowing the value of life, how could he not know the cost of death? Each death held a debt so that life could be rich and beautiful. To pay the debt, and keep life flowing, the sacred hunters and warriors needed to be blessed by the females. As she passed that which she had brought from the void into his hands, to be taken into the world, he needed to be blessed so that he became part of that which gave life. Then, when he killed, he could, in turn, bless the life he took. This sacred gift, from the Earth, could then enrich the lives of those who consumed it and so the circle of life and death turned and each played their part in the sacred dance.

But at some point, men and women had stepped away from each other: the sacred hunters and warriors became brutal killers in the eyes of the birthers - who felt righteous in bringing life forth. But that same life was sustained by consuming the unblessed, that which had been torn from the Earth without a care for the mother of all things.

The more unacknowledged the grief, the greater the burden. Without the home of ritual space to live in, the grief ate into the hearts of the people until they felt empty, angry or cynical of the holy and all looked for scapegoats. The mythology of the brutal male grew to fill the need to blame. The males carried this burden on their shoulders, bowed down by the weight.

But the need to live pressed at their bellies. The males still needed to ensure survival. But now, when the hunters returned, it was not to a hero's welcome. Even as they brought home their bounty, they received the knowledge that they were crueller, baser, less human. As they crawled on their bellies to the centre fires of human existence, dragging their bloody kill and offering it to the people, they felt the weight of being male - the provider and protector.

But the rainbow bridge unites and what befalls one befalls all. The males had no choice but to keep slogging in the world, but the female had fallen out of love with him. The females kept bringing forth life and needed it maintained, but for this, they felt shame.

The woman felt all these layers of meaning, as she looked at the simple drawing in the dirt. She remembered the pull of attraction through the opposite poles that had united her and knew that, if twisted, it could just as easily have been repulsion.

What had made the two step away from each other? And yet, without it, the rainbow bridge would not have formed.

She felt the grief spread through her body, flowing freely now it was not impinged by guilt or shame. She felt such a deep respect for the burden carriers. She realised forests needed planting, in which they could heal their wounds, to be honoured for the life they had endured, to be made whole, to find a way to pay the debt, so that they ceased to be destroyers of the holy and became instead its champions. Forests made of abundant blessing, forests made of love and respect, forests deep and green and fragrant with forgiveness.

The waves of grief continued to roll through the woman. As they did, she felt the connection to the masculine inside of her, for the men she loved and for those in the world beyond her world.

She thought of those she felt superior to, the modern day sin eaters: those that bloodied their hands on the suffering of others; those who heard the screams of trees as they chain sawed them down, to provide the wood she ran her hands along with pleasure; those that destroyed the habitats of wild animals, so that people like her could enjoy opulent vegetarian cuisine; those who blasted the earth for rocks and stones and crystals for her to use for good ambience and healing.

Her heart was now open to these unblessed males who lived with death so that she didn't have to. She needed to start by blessing them. Then one day, if the forests of blessing grew lush enough, they would bless the lives they took.

She could no longer hid herself that she was innocent. The rainbow united them, and she had eaten the fruits of their pillaging.

She was alive, but it was through the death of others.

She needed to appreciate the gift of sacrifice. She needed to rejoin the circle and allow the blessings to flow. She was a birther and a visioner of truth and beauty. The truth was she was the butcher, the logger, the abattoir worker, the slash and burner. She was human, and until she acknowledged the holy, then she was the brutal killer. But she could transform them back to the sacred hunter and warrior. Her tears needed weaving into the rainbow ribbon bridge.

It was a start, and from there, she would know where next.

The wisdom keepers held her now. They knew that she had seen the meaning of the symbol. They took her to their dwelling in the woods. It was a round hut and there lived the Grandmothers who wove the rainbow shawl. They spun the threads from the stories of humanity and wove them together into the fabric of human existence. Every tear shed was held in the rainbow shawl. The Grandmothers told their stories swiftly, their nimble fingers weaving the words into the ever growing blanket.

The woman watched the old ones working. She saw them weave her story into their work, such a tiny part of the vast whole. The Grandmothers held their focus to ensure every story was included. They had no time to make judgements on the merits; there were no heroes or villains, just experience. Each story revealed its truth and beauty as the light of spirit penetrated the tears, breaking them into

The violence that continued to roll through the man

the colours of the spectrum.

Why the shawl, she thought? Does it have any other purpose? Maybe...

But she got no further with her wondering. The Grandmothers took her outside and lay her on the blanket. She watched as the Grandmothers held one side, then the Grandfathers came and took the opposite side. They picked her up and rocked her gently, like a baby in a cradle. The wisdom of her experience rolled around her until it found a place to sit inside of her.

She surrendered to the rhythm of being rocked by the wisdom keepers, the weavers of the shawl of human experience, until she fell asleep.

The woman journeyed through the land of her dreams, until she awoke the next day, home and alone.

Her grief still roamed her body. Its stories needed telling and blessings needed to be given. She felt so overwhelmed that she went to her special place in the trees. She sang to White Buffalo Calf Woman asking for help. The sacred woman came, bringing Miracle, the buffalo*. The woman laid her face on the buffalo's face and sang and cried until she could sing no more, and then, she just cried. The tears hurt as they ripped through her body, but the release was immense.

The buffalo's face was now wet with the woman's tears. The woman cried and kissed Miracle's beautiful face, stroking the wet fur. Her eyes met the buffalo's huge eyes. In that moment, the woman was told the story of sacrifice, by the beast that stood solidly in front of her.

The graciousness of Miracle made the woman sob more. Here were the stories of how humans stole from the Earth, but Miracle was telling her, nothing can be stolen if freely given. The graciousness to receive the gift is all that is required.

The woman felt the humility of knowing that, indeed, human beings are just part of the family of Earth - not greater, not smaller - just a part of its beautiful diverse richness. She saw how humans impoverished themselves with their arrogance, with their guilt and with their refusal to take responsibility to attend to their grief, born from the indebtedness to that which sings all life here.

Miracle continued to give herself to the woman as a generous, steady presence. Bearing witness to the woman's chaos; not taking it from her but letting the woman's tears roll down her face; not judging her, not rescuing her but inviting her back into the circle, inviting her to step into the bigger picture.

The woman sang again to White Buffalo Calf woman, calling for wisdom, calling for grace, calling for vision and calling for peace. As she sang, she heard White Buffalo Calf woman telling her to let go of the guilt and the grief. Now was the time to stand in her power.

What is the power of woman?

She fetched her newly potted trees and watered them with her tears. They would make rainbows to tickle the new shoots and bless their vulnerability. She thanked White Buffalo Calf woman and Miracle and bade them farewell. It was time now for the last leg of her journey.

She sat on the earth, asking to be in her power. The small trees sat in a circle about her, rising up to the light, but it was down that she needed to go.

A mighty taproot grew from her, pushing down into the dark earth. This was her power. She climbed down her own root. Further and faster and deeper she went. She passed a golden dragon asleep in the Earth, but this was not her stop. On she went, further, faster, deeper until she heard it. She hadn't known what it was she was seeking, until she heard the heartbeat of the earth.

She moved towards the sound until it enveloped her. Here it was pink and pulsating to the rhythm of the heartbeat. The woman pulled her root right down into the throbbing heart and the Rhythm danced through her.

---

* White Buffalo Calf Woman is the sacred woman of supernatural origin within Lakota Sioux mythology, who gave the people their seven sacred rituals, the most well known of which is the pipe ceremony.

The female white buffalo calf, Miracle, who was born in 1994 was seen by the Lakota elders as the awaited sign that the time had arrived in which human beings are to be held accountable to their adherence and honouring of these sacred teachings.

She was female, but somewhere inside lived her noble warrior. She was human, but she was also spirit. She was part of the rich diversity of the Earth family and she was also part of the "oneness."

All the opposites began to back in to one another and merge. The rainbow colours merged, and all that was left was white light.

She saw other taproots that had become disconnected from the One Heart. She encouraged them in by singing a song that came to her:

In love we sit
In love we mend
This love we weave
This love we send

Some roots moved towards the sound of her singing. For others, it was not yet their time, but some day, all would be anchored here and the rainbow shawl would be complete. Who knew where it would them make a bridge to?

Now it was time to journey back up into her body. A female body that knew not all was right in the relationship between men and women, but maybe one day she would stop forgetting what she already knew. Until then, she needed to accept herself and celebrate her ability to cry.

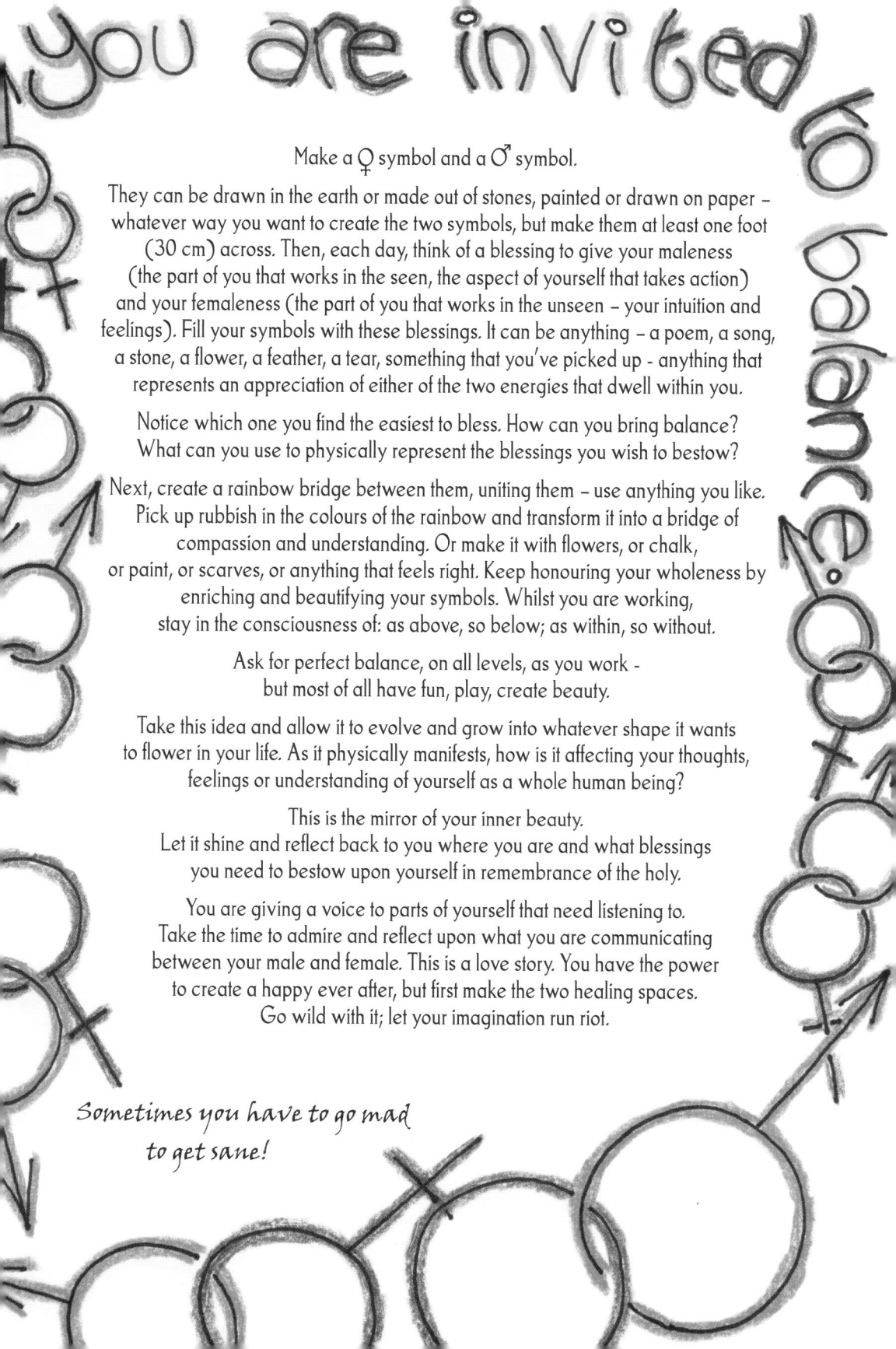

Make a ♀ symbol and a ♂ symbol.

They can be drawn in the earth or made out of stones, painted or drawn on paper –
whatever way you want to create the two symbols, but make them at least one foot
(30 cm) across. Then, each day, think of a blessing to give your maleness
(the part of you that works in the seen, the aspect of yourself that takes action)
and your femaleness (the part of you that works in the unseen – your intuition and
feelings). Fill your symbols with these blessings. It can be anything – a poem, a song,
a stone, a flower, a feather, a tear, something that you've picked up – anything that
represents an appreciation of either of the two energies that dwell within you.

Notice which one you find the easiest to bless. How can you bring balance?
What can you use to physically represent the blessings you wish to bestow?

Next, create a rainbow bridge between them, uniting them – use anything you like.
Pick up rubbish in the colours of the rainbow and transform it into a bridge of
compassion and understanding. Or make it with flowers, or chalk,
or paint, or scarves, or anything that feels right. Keep honouring your wholeness by
enriching and beautifying your symbols. Whilst you are working,
stay in the consciousness of: as above, so below; as within, so without.

Ask for perfect balance, on all levels, as you work -
but most of all have fun, play, create beauty.

Take this idea and allow it to evolve and grow into whatever shape it wants
to flower in your life. As it physically manifests, how is it affecting your thoughts,
feelings or understanding of yourself as a whole human being?

This is the mirror of your inner beauty.
Let it shine and reflect back to you where you are and what blessings
you need to bestow upon yourself in remembrance of the holy.

You are giving a voice to parts of yourself that need listening to.
Take the time to admire and reflect upon what you are communicating
between your male and female. This is a love story. You have the power
to create a happy ever after, but first make the two healing spaces.
Go wild with it; let your imagination run riot.

Sometimes you have to go mad
to get sane!

The North-easterly place
between Death and Life...

Under the wings of the bird of quiet lived joy and light. Under her wings lived hope.

Introduction

This journey was made on the same day as the
"Truth and Beauty" journey.
I was sitting in the northeast of this circle of women –
for me, the place between death and life.
I wanted to explore what that meant – not literal death,
but the many little deaths that are experienced.
The end of one chapter before another begins.
How does truth and beauty traverse this space in the northeast?
What are its teachings?

I'd picked a truth card before making the journey, which read:

"Beauty is in each heart, in every living thing.
This beauty is the universal essence of that being's creation."

This felt like a massive confirmation of my previous exploration.
But what happens when the truth doesn't look so beautiful?
What happens in death? How could I see beyond the tyranny of the
positive to the beautiful truth of the perfect ever-moving circle of life?
What about the beauty that is painful to look at?
Not comfortable, but real nevertheless.
I was obviously having a little trouble with letting go.

Death and insanity were challenging, but like the thirteenth
fairy in Sleeping Beauty, I needed to invite them in,
to receive the gift of their blessing. To wake up to my truth,
my beauty, all thirteen fairies were needed.

There was once a woman who found herself journeying northeast as a salmon.

She knew that beauty is in every thing, held at the centre of creation.

But what, exactly, did this mean?

To find the answer she swam up the river, as one of many salmon. She felt her strength and vigour as she battled against the current, up waterfalls, catching her breath in still pools before continuing onwards.

She knew she was not alone in the feeling that she was swimming home. The other salmon that she swam with seemed to share the same determination to find the place of their hatching, or to die in the attempt.

The further she travelled, the less interested she became in anything that distracted her until eventually, she arrived at the place of her birth. As she did, she became a woman once more.

She sat in the pool of still water. Trees lined the bank of her stretch of river and the roots of a particularly large one became her submerged seat.

She watched her travelling companions spawn and then die. Their journey was complete; their cycle had reached full turn. She watched, realising that this was the pool that sat between death and life. She was held in the pause - the time when one thing is let go of, but the new thing has not yet been grasped.

She watched the dead salmon floating in the water; the eggs they had spawned seemingly dead, their new life not yet ready to reveal itself to the world.

She didn't know what to do or how to be in this place. It seemed hardly a blink of an eye since she had felt such a deep driving need to be here. Now that she was here… what? So she sat in the pool, between death and life, until night came and with it, the moon.

The next day, bears and other creatures came and ate up the dead salmon. The woman climbed from the pool that she had sat in and walked the riverbanks. She collected armfuls of wild flowers, which she threw into the water, honouring the sacrifice that she had witnessed: the sacrifice that ensured the continuance of the great cycle.

Eventually, the eggs began to hatch. The salmon fry, eager for their new lives to begin, teemed in the water. Once again, the woman became a salmon, this time a fry, and full of hope rather than power.

The little salmon joined the others in their journey back to the sea. As she swam, she felt the love of the parent salmon as they swam in the Spirit River above them, watching over them and welcoming any of their babies, consumed by the journey, into their numbers.

Eventually, the woman salmon reached the sea. She grew wise and strong. Then, one day, she felt the pull to return up river: to return home. She knew her soul was like this; only in death was it released to return home.

She returned to her woman body then. She watched as the seasons turned, like a beautiful flower, giving its sweet fragility to the world; knowing the point of full blossoming was also the pause before the fall; petals browning and shrivelling, Seed heads swelling, ensuring the essence's continuance in the still centre as all else danced between death and life.

The woman felt a heaviness in her heart. The certainty that everything dies was no protection. The grief she held belonged to her. She felt the familiarity of it. She held it for everything in her life that had died. Even for that which had fertilised the new seeds, the grief still weighed her down.

But it was more than just her personal burden. She had also inherited ancestral and cultural grief. She was part of many cycles and circles, for better and for worse. She needed to surrender in order to find the seeds of light and hope. As she thought this, she felt herself crack open along her front, like a pea pod being popped. Inside, she was filled with tiny black

seeds. In the pool between death and until night came and with it, the moon, So she set off...

seeds that fell out upon the ground, scattering themselves in the rich, fertile soil of her acknowledged grief.

The seeds began to sprout. As each one pushed itself through the soil, a beam of light grew out of the Earth, until it looked as if the sun itself was rising from the land. As the shoots became stronger, the light beams intensified. Now, as the woman looked, the spirit salmon were swimming through the beams, weaving in and out of the warps of rising light.

She walked into the weaving and felt the wonder.

"Wonder."

She said it over and over to herself. She felt its meaning rising up from the Earth. The One-der was the acknowledgement of the oneness; the knowing that everything is connected, the appreciation of the beauty and diversity of the fragmented One. She realised the space between death and life completed the great hoop. She knew she was part of it - how could she not be? It was everything. She wanted to help weave the light.

As she thought this, a great black bird came to her and she climbed on to its back. They flew through the air, twisting in and out of the light beams. She opened her chest and the grief started to pour out like a strange but wonderful crop-spraying plane.

She fed the seeds from her heavy heart, fertilising them. As she did so, her heart emptied. The emptier it became, the lighter it got, until there was no more heaviness to come out, and then she fed the seeds with the lightness of her heart. As the bird flew insanely on, looping the loop, weaving and spinning, a song began to need singing. She realised she was riding on the back of the bird of grief. Under the great, black joy and light and hope. But these were only revealed when she flew. There was no choice with the grief bird. She had to fly her or hope and light would remain tucked away under the wings of the great, black bird. The song pushed harder. It was a mad song, a sad song, a grief song; not a light song or a joy song but a mad song, a sad song. But under her wings lived joy and light. Under her wings lived hope.

The song went on and on. The woman felt the madness of it. The whole of her felt the loop. Which way was up? Which way was down? Ordinary rules didn't apply here, in this space between death and life, in the formless place without structure, where the new life was not yet ready to reveal itself.

Yes, it was mad, but the madness wasn't bad, it was the only way to become sane.

The great bird soared through the air, its wings fully unfolded, and from beneath its wings, it released light and joy and hope. From the insanity of riding the grief bird, the woman knew that beauty was in each heart, in every living thing and that this beauty was the universal essence of that being's creation.

Beauty was the truth of every living thing. The truth was that they would live and die and the dance would ensure their immortality. It was a dance of wonder. Sometimes it seemed mad and sometimes sane. The steps changed, but the rhythm held it all together, as the great heartbeat of the Universe.

grief
needs
space.

We live in cycles within cycles.
Endings and beginnings are a part of all of our lives.
Create a space to grieve – it will feed the birth of the next phase.
It could be the end of summer or the children starting school or leaving home.
It could be the end of a way of life, a love, a break with a bad habit, the loss of a loved one – or the hundreds of other little losses we experience within our lives.

Riding the Grief Bird

Find a comfortable space to sit or lie where you won't be disturbed (remember to turn off phones). Shut your eyes and concentrate on your breathing – breathing in the sweet breath of life. Breathing out anything that distorts or impedes the flow of energy through and around you. With each breath, you soften a little more, relaxing and letting go. Breathing deeper, release any tensions, filling your lungs with life force.
From your lungs, it enters your bloodstream and then into every cell of your body, each cell fed by the sweet breath of life.
Visualise yourself outside on a grassy hillock. Have a good look around.
Notice the landscape. What time of day is it? What season? What else is there to see?
Are there any trees, or any other plants? What's the weather like?
Keep breathing in this space – notice how the air feels here.
Then, call to the grief bird. Notice it in the distance, flying directly towards you.
Watch it get closer. Now, it's landed right next to you. It invites you to ride on its back.
It is so close, you can see the joy and light and hope tucked under its wings.
It holds these as a gift for you, but you need to ride on its back first.
As you climb on, you see how easy it is to hold on for the ride.
Enjoy feeling your courage mount, as the bird starts to take to the air.
You notice that your body has opened up, and wherever you are storing any grief, it starts to pour out of you, releasing the burden of unexpressed grief.
You notice that the bird flies in exactly the right way to support you and enable you to let go.

you are invited to release

Trust the bird.
If the flight rolls you around, go with it.
If it soars up or swoops down, just keep releasing and letting go.
Make sounds to help you.

The more you release, the brighter becomes the light of joy and hope.
Feel the wonder; you are part of everything. The energy trapped in your body,
through grief, is part of everything and you are setting it free to return
to the great ever-moving circle of life.
Once you have emptied yourself out, the light from
beneath the bird's wings starts to fill your body.
Celebrate that joy; feel the peace in your soul that hope brings.
You fill yourself so completely that light and joy and hope bubble through and out
of you, blessing life, blessing your journey and feeding the seeds of your future so
that they grow fat and start to shoot in your life, creating a beautiful new beginning.
Keep riding the grief bird as long as you like.

It's now time to land.
You come gently to Earth and climb from your bird's back.
She lifts one of her wings and invites you in, holding you like one of her chicks,
tenderly tucking you under her wing.
Under here is pure joy and you completely fill yourself with this light and hope,
which takes you to a place of deep, penetrating peace.
Breathe deeply again and again and again...
Start to be aware of your physical body, feeling your fingers and toes.
Be aware of your breath entering and leaving your body.
Become aware of the temperature of the air on your skin,
the sounds within the room.

Take one more deep breath of joy, light and hope and then,
when you are ready,

open your eyes.

One morning a woman woke
up with the dearest wish to
find the dancing child that
lived in her heart...

...dancing the woman found her way back home to the place that nurtured her. What a dance was danced and in that...

Introduction

The original question that I asked to make the journey that this story is based upon was: "How may I gain a teaching on what I can do to best work with the dancing child in my heart, to show my love and respect?"

What a mouthful! I'd picked up a card for myself, from my inner child cards, and drawn the three of hearts. This card talks about the mysterious rhythm and magic dance of the deep waters.

It encouraged the discovery of the little child who resides in the cave of my heart to let her know how much she is loved and cherished, and to honour the intimate dance that we share.
But seeing as before I'd picked up this card I'd never even known of there being a small child in my heart, let alone a dancing one, I thought I'd like to investigate more.

I liked the sound of her and I was keen for us to dance together.
As usual, most of my journeying was a tool for an ordinary woman to fathom the simplest way to navigate the path of 'getting real'.

The prospect of touching in with this child excited me.
I'd been living a 'grown-up' life full of responsibilities
– school time tables and committee meetings –
and a flirtation with the mysterious rhythm and
magic dance of the deep waters sounded
better than a weekend by the seaside.
But, how to go about it?
And so, I journeyed.

One morning, a woman woke up with the dearest wish to find the dancing child that lived in her heart. It had been a long time since the woman had sat with her, had bathed in the beauty of her presence. The more she thought about her, the more she knew that today was the day to make that journey.

Through the shell of this world she broke, and came to a place of sand and desert. She called out to her dancing child, who lived in her heart. She asked for a lesson to show her how to be with love and respect. She waited. Nobody came. So, she climbed to the top of the rim of the desert basin. In the distance she saw a small group making their way across the sands.

They were too small, at first, to be seen properly. As she moved to meet them, she saw that some rode on camels but others were being dragged behind on their bellies, like tin cans behind a honeymoon car.

The woman was shocked to see such brutality. As she came closer, she could see that the ones being dragged were smiling, their faces ecstatic.

Then she was amongst them; she could now see their sand-filled eyes and mouths. She could see where the ropes burned their wrists, and the sand blotting their blood stained wounds. But most of all, she saw their smiling, happy, accepting faces. She was deeply confused. She asked the dragged ones what was happening.

"We're on a journey to enlightenment," they replied.

Now they neared the top of a large ridge. As the camel riders reached the top, they stopped and the woman was able to catch them up.

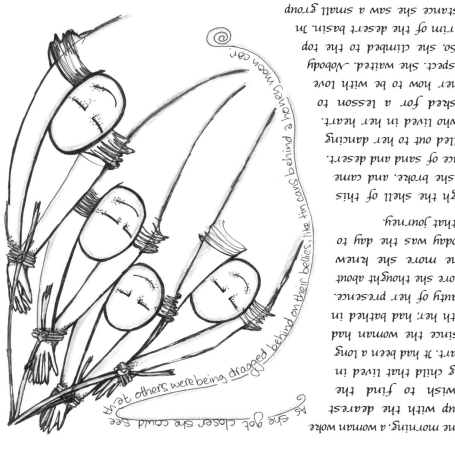

As she got closer she could see that others were being dragged behind on their bellies, like tin cans behind a honey moon car

She asked the camel riders who they were. They explained that they were making a journey to the City with their students. As they said this, they turned their gaze out and beyond. The woman followed their gaze and saw the City far off in the distance.

The woman told of her own quest and asked the camel riders if they thought the City would hold the answers.

"Yes, come to the city with us," they said, "There are many great teachers of enlightenment in the City."

The woman didn't feel certain; she sensed something not right about this group, but they seemed good hearted folk and she had no better offers - so, off she went with them, across the sands on their way to the far off City.

Night started to announce its arrival. As the day said its farewells, they came to a place of plenty, an oasis in the desert.

The next morning, the woman awoke and went for a look around. She watched the camel riders dragging the light-seekers on to sun beds around the sparkling pool. They were unable to do anything for themselves, other than smile.

The camel riders saw to their needs and attended them well.

The woman went and lay with them for a while but she just didn't get it! Her mind wandered off but was brought back by the arrival of the oasis children coming to bathe in the shimmering waters.

She enjoyed the sights and sounds of the children playing in the pool. She remembered her dancing child in her heart that she yearned to see.

She went to join the children.

They were beautiful, with large brown eyes, and full of fun. She played with them and laughed with them, drank their beauty and filled herself with their trusting innocence.

She looked amongst them for her dancing child, but did not find her.

Then she noticed an old, old woman walk past the pool. The children didn't stop playing; the light-seekers didn't stop smiling, but for the woman, everything, just for a second, seemed to stand still.

She hardly dare ask if this could be her dancing child that lived in her heart. Surely it hadn't been that long since she had visited her! In her dismay and confusion, she asked for a sign to help her. At that moment, a raven flew down and travelled along with the old hag, who was now walking towards the mountains on the other side of the oasis. She knew then that she had to follow.

The children were sad to see her go. They tugged at her heart; it would have been so good to stay here with them and bathe in the pools of their brown eyes.

She didn't want them upset, but despite their cries, she climbed from the water and followed the hag who had now disappeared amongst the cragginess of the mountain's feet. Soon she heard the fun-filled laughter as the children once again resumed their play. Then, the oasis was behind her.

The climb was steep and the way uncertain, but every now and then she caught a glimpse of the raven, usually when she felt overwhelmed with frustration at not knowing where, or even why, she was going.

It was in those moments that the woman caught a glimpse of the raven's glossy feathers or heard its frog-like call. The raven spoke of magic in its throaty rasp.

Eventually, the raven saw her to the top of the mountain.

Here the old hag sat, her legs dangling over the precipice. She looked out and over the world. The raven invited the woman to come and sit with them. She did, fascinated still by this ancient one.

Before she could censor herself, she asked the old hag why she was so ugly. She blushed as she heard

141

herself say the words – shame and awkwardness burned her cheeks with the stark honesty of her question. But the old woman took no offence and replied:

"I look like I'm expected to look, like an ugly, warty witch." The old woman enjoyed the words, as she rolled them around her mouth, playfully bouncing them out into the world, as if inviting a game of catch.

Then the old hag lay back and sighed deeply in contentment.

"Beautifull," she said, and allowed the word to dance in the air about her face before the breeze took it to the four corners and spread her message to all that could hear with the ear of the heart.

The woman looked and saw that, indeed, this old hag was beautiful and a beautiful child danced in her heart.

The old woman lay with her back to the Earth Mother and looked to the Sky Father. She knew she was daughter to them both.

Her legs still hung over the sheer drop, but she was so comfortable in her skin, that all she could see was beauty.

The woman watched the crone turn her ear to the ground – all the better to hear the teachings of rock and stone. Here, with her ear to the ribs of the Earth, the old woman heard the Mother's heart beating. Like a child at the breast, she lay, here, she learned from the mountain about the things that nurtured her and where to put her trust.

The woman lay down next to the hag and listened for the rhythm of life that pulsated through the mountain.

Then she gently asked the old woman how to be with the dancing child in her heart with love and respect. The old woman turned her face and looked in to her eyes:

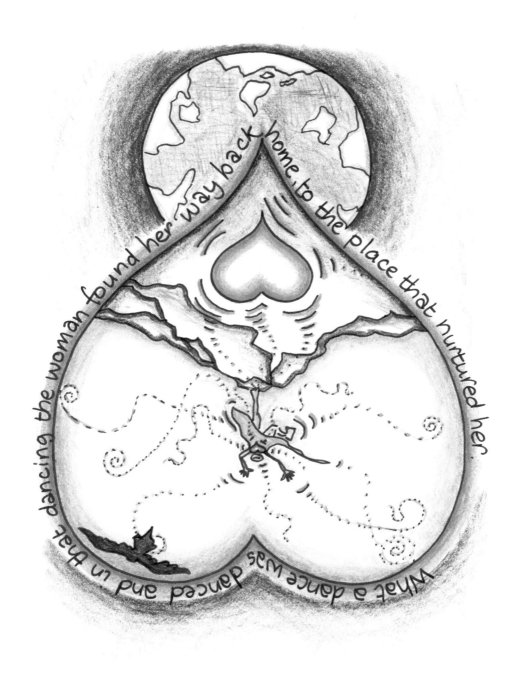

Verses of love and verses of respect danced through her.

What a dance was danced, and in that dancing, the woman found her way back home to the place that nurtured her; to the place in which her trust was held safe.

"Listen," she said.

The woman listened - she heard the heartbeat of the Earth. Then, singing the chorus, she heard a child's voice. She felt a stirring in her heart.

you are invited to dance.

It's time to dance.

Choose a piece of music that you love from your childhood, a piece that makes you feel happy and optimistic. Choose simple, loving music – not teenage angst stuff. When my daughter was young, she danced herself well to 'The Best of the Drifters'.

Make a dancing date with yourself. Clear the space on all levels. Push back the furniture, turn off the phone, make sure no one will disturb you for half an hour or so. You may want to dress up or down (dressing up as you did when you were little and played make believe). Make it a fun part of this celebration of your dancing child.

Then, just dance.

No one is watching. You are dancing for yourself, so how does your body want to move? You can be wild, soft, sexy or ugly.
It really doesn't matter what you look like.
But it does matter how it feels from the inside.

You can dance yourself into freedom or wellness or understanding or love or whatever good feelings you want to create today in your life. Shift your body, create change. You can pose a question, or dilemma, that's making you feel stuck. Put it out to the Universe, then move. Creative solutions will then come to you.

The most important thing is to have fun. Let joy heal you. The most healing part of this is to give yourself the space to play in. Even if your body is unable to move, you can visualise this exercise.

At the end, take a quiet space to hold yourself in. Cherish the beautiful child spirit you hold within yourself. Acknowledge the wisdom of innocence, then skip into your life, taking your child self with you. Play at being you and see what changes need putting in place so that you sparkle more.

You are beautiful.

Grandmother Joy

"What do you do Grandma?" "I put the shine on things."

She lived in a state of grace, welcoming all that came, rubbing it across her chest till it shone.

Introduction

I first met Grandmother Joy back in 2002.
Or, should I say, I first consciously met her at that time.
In truth, she's been whispering her wisdom to me all my life.

At that time, I was assistant to Annie, who held the North of the
Grandmother's circle. We travelled from west Wales to Norfolk to hold a
circle there. The journey was extraordinary. We had been talking so much
that we missed the turning on to the M25 and so had to navigate our way
through London without a map. But we did have a feather!
We intuited our way across the city, allowing the feather to point the way.

It was a Friday afternoon and so we hit a good many traffic jams.
Because we didn't know where we were going, we decided we couldn't
get lost: you can only get lost if you know where you should be.

We giggled our way through the metropolis.
Each standstill in traffic was an opportunity to sing the 'One Heart" song,
at the top of our voices with the doors open so we could ground the
energy into the city streets through our feet.

We received many strange looks but we were in such a playful mood
that everything increased the joyful adventure. We saw signs and omens
in the ordinary and mundane to guide us. It was one of the first times that I
touched the joyful spirit of London and felt the innocence of the city.

We made our way through in good time; very little petrol was used during
this period and we both felt exhilarated by experiencing London's spirit.

The next day we ran the circle and I met Grandmother Joy,
officially, for the first time. This is the story of that first meeting.
Grandmother Joy has tucked me under her wing and
I've continued to work with her ever since.

A couple of years ago, our relationship deepened and I got to feel her
energy on a deeper level; I now know her as Grandmother Light Joy.
The deeper the energy work, the more Light Joy is needed.
She is there through the mundane and ordinary,
putting her shine on things, hunting the Killjoys,
and helping to bring me more fully into my natural self.

There was once a woman who surfed to the One Heart on a pink wave. Her surfing led her to a beach on a small island. Built at the forest edge, upon the white sand, stood a moonhut.

The woman asked for permission to enter and was invited in by Grandmother Joy. The woman asked for healing and was laid down and tickled all over with a downy feather; then the ancient one rolled her on to her front and lay down upon the woman.

She told the woman she was going to merge with her so that she could experience being Grandmother Joy. She entered the woman through the back of her heart. The woman ran from the moonhut with Grandmother Joy in her heart and threw herself into the sea's heaving waves.

The ocean pulled and pushed her about, waking her up, until she knew what it was like to be alive. She felt her life-force growing as a smile of exhilaration spread across her face. She battled with the sea, sometimes losing and being bashed upon outcrops of rock that ripped at her ankles. The salty sting led her to new heights of ecstatic joy.

She couldn't slumber here, half asleep in her comfort zone; here life called to her and invited her to play. She shrieked and whooped and threw herself into the waves. A big wave came and pulled her into its tumbling roll. Disorientated in the wave's embrace, her lungs longed for the breath of life. When it came, it reminded her sweetly of the first breath she had taken upon being born. This breath reminded her of the pain, the fear and the sorrow of being in a body, the yardstick by which we measure the joy, the beauty and the harmony of merging spirit with form.

Eventually, exhausted from the rough and tumble with her watery playmate, she crawled to the shore, panting through her broad smile. Yes, it was good to be really

She couldn't slumber here, half asleep in her comfort zone; here life called to her and invited her to play alive, and now she needed the peace, stability and warmth of the beach, a mother's lap on which to curl up for the moment. She lay panting on the warm sand, feeling the water lapping at her feet, inviting her back in to play. "Not now," she thought, "another time."

The two women separated. As they looked at each other, a knowing had grown between them.

"What do you do?" the woman asked the beautifully alive old woman.

"I put the shine on things," Grandmother replied.

The woman looked at her. "How?" she asked.

"Like this," Grandmother replied, as she breathed on to an invisible object and rubbed it across her bosom.

"What sort of things?" the woman asked.

"Oh, everything, anything - dreams, ideas, objects, places, memories, beings. Do you want to be my shining apprentice?"

The young woman looked down at her less than ample bosom, but as she did, her breasts began to grow. As she looked from her chest to Grandmother Joy, the old woman's eyes twinkled.

"You need the right equipment for the job," she said.

The two women set off and along the way they stopped to breathe on and rub things across their bosoms. The woman watched Grandmother Joy; life for her was an abundant blessing. She lived in a state of grace, welcoming all that came, rubbing it across her chest until it shone, so that its gift became apparent no matter how much it disguised itself.

"Is that all you do?" asked the woman, as she breathed and shone an idea that she had.

"What do you do Grandma?" "I put the shine on things."
she lived in a state of grace, welcoming all that came, rubbing it across her chest till it shone.

"Oh no," replied the old woman, "I also hunt the Killjoys."

The woman looked up and caught the deep passion in the old woman's eyes; a light shone from them, older than time, a light from the original flame. The woman asked about the Killjoys; she had known a few in her life, and at times had been one herself.

"Oh, the Killjoys are not people, but people can become infected with them. They are culturally inherited burdens that are taken out of a misplaced notion of duty and respectability. People are naturally joyous," Grandmother said, "But sadly, people are no longer very natural. To hunt the Killjoys and polish the shine is only to bring you back to your natural state of grace. Joyousness should not be a guilty indulgence, it is a way of bringing light into the world for all - it is part of the truth and beauty of who you are."

The woman noticed that while they had been talking, they had walked back to the moonhut. The old woman took down a bow and a set of arrows from the wall and they went out again and entered the forest.

Grandmother Joy stalked an invisible prey and the woman mimicked her stance. The two of them slid silently through the trees. This beautiful Grandmother fascinated the woman; she copied her stealth, adoring her, loving her. Yes, she realised that she loved her.

At that moment, they reached a clearing and Grandmother Joy stood up straight, relaxing her posture and broadening her focus.

The woman looked her shyly in the eyes and asked "You are real, aren't you?" She so wanted her to be, but she carried the scars of being talked into believing that her reality was merely her imagination.

Grandmother Joy looked at her and proclaimed, "You're having an attack of the Killjoys!" She grabbed the woman's wrist and pulled her back to the beach where she dug a deep, deep hole. The woman looked on, perplexed, for she had been carrying the thing they had been hunting and not realised it.

Once the hole was dug, Grandmother proceeded to slap at the woman's back and chest and little pieces fell from her into the hole. Grandmother Joy stopped. She squared up to the woman, her eyes twinkling, and announced, "There's a much quicker way." She pushed the woman into the hole and quickly shovelled the sand on to her: "Only the joy is light enough to rise up - the Killjoys will be trapped."

As the woman lay in her grave, she felt the invitation from Grandmother Joy to rise up through the sand. She knew she left something behind in the darkness, but it was nothing she wanted. She could feel a new brightness and lightness dancing around her being.

The two then walked down the beach, collecting shells. Only the most ornate and curly ones were right for their purpose.

Back to the grave they went and in the most richly, beautiful, honouring way they could, they spelled out "R.I.P." on the grave of the Killjoys.

They danced, and the beat of their feet drummed the earth. They danced for joy on the grave of the Killjoys. They danced for life and love and beauty and the truth of who they naturally were.

Tired from dancing, they returned to the moonhut, and as the woman brushed the Grandmother's hair, she asked the old lady if there was anything she could do for her.

"My wood pile needs replenishing."

Soon they slept.

The next morning, the woman arose, went to the forest and pulled and dragged all the fallen branches she could find. She panted and sweated and thought of the beautiful old woman who would warm herself whilst burning this wood. All day she laboured until the wood pile was filled to capacity, neatly sawn and lovingly ordered. She

stood back from her work with a great sense of accomplishment. The glow of satisfaction was great upon her.

Grandmother Joy, who she hadn't seen all day, now came towards her and placed an arm around her shoulder.

"Yes, work is joyous, when we give our gift open-heartedly." As they hugged, the woman felt what had been meant. She knew she had reached completion for now and it was time to take her leave, to bring back to her life all that she had learned.

She felt both excited and afraid to go, but one thing she knew for sure - this was real.

152

you are invited to Bless

Invite Grandmother Joy into your life;
become her shining apprentice.

Take a walk. It may be a route you know really well –
the walk to school to pick up the kids, the way to work, or walking the dog.
But this time, invite Grandmother Joy to walk with you.

As you go, see things through her eyes. Notice anything that needs shining
and imagine yourself giving it a lovely polish.

If your children are young, they may want to play with you
or you may wish to play by yourself for now.

Notice how the world looks to Grandmother Joy –
see the magic, see the beauty,
see the world that is just a polish away from the Garden of Eden.
You've been walking in it all your life.

Don't give energy to what needs to diminish –
just notice what needs to grow and let it flower in your heart.

You can hunt the Killjoys by just quickly, but firmly, saying "No" to them;
then put your full attention back to the magic and beauty
that is revealing itself to you.

You can do this any time you need, but try to make it a good habit –
a habit you can become addicted to.

Walk lightly, laugh at yourself, but also let Grandmother Joy cuddle you to her.
One day, you will no longer be her shining apprentice;
you will be a fully fledged mistress of the art of walking for joy.

May your heart be fat with sunshine.

Acknowledgements

Big thank-yous to:

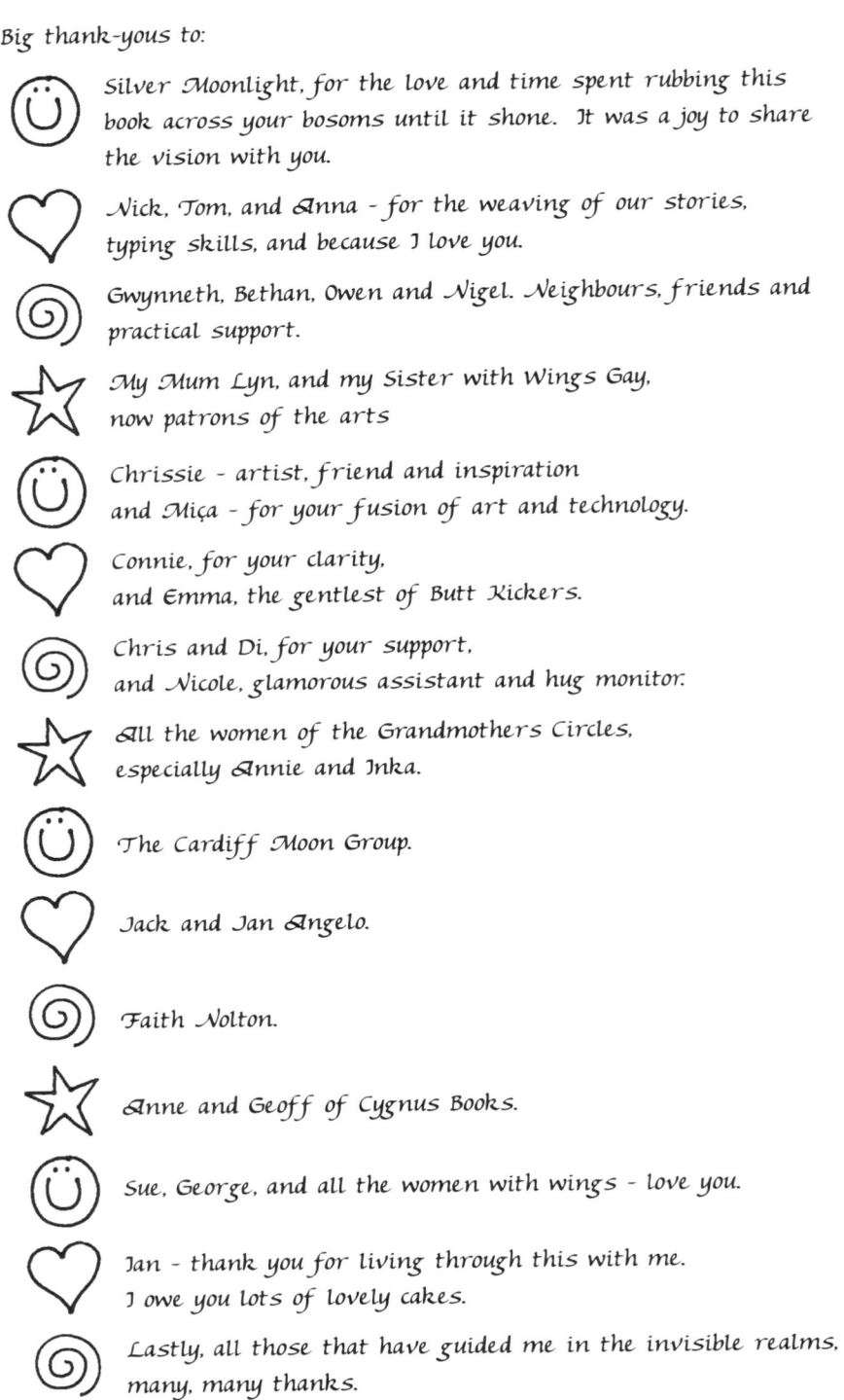

Silver Moonlight, for the love and time spent rubbing this book across your bosoms until it shone. It was a joy to share the vision with you.

Nick, Tom, and Anna - for the weaving of our stories, typing skills, and because I love you.

Gwynneth, Bethan, Owen and Nigel. Neighbours, friends and practical support.

My Mum Lyn, and my Sister with Wings Gay, now patrons of the arts

Chrissie - artist, friend and inspiration and Mica - for your fusion of art and technology.

Connie, for your clarity, and Emma, the gentlest of Butt Kickers.

Chris and Di, for your support, and Nicole, glamorous assistant and hug monitor.

All the women of the Grandmothers Circles, especially Annie and Inka.

The Cardiff Moon Group.

Jack and Jan Angelo.

Faith Nolton.

Anne and Geoff of Cygnus Books.

Sue, George, and all the women with wings - love you.

Jan - thank you for living through this with me. I owe you lots of lovely cakes.

Lastly, all those that have guided me in the invisible realms, many, many thanks.

Join our online community, and share your inspirations and
experiences of these tales.

~

Connect with others who have also made this journey.

You can also order extra copies of this book
and purchase high quality prints of the 13 canvases,
to bring tranquillity to your meditation room, joy to your kitchen,
and beauty to... wherever you wish.

~

For all this, for information on workshops and events,

and to join our mailing list please visit

www.shewhofindsgold.net

About the Author

Manda Clements, now in her early 50s and living in West Wales, feels that her main job has been to identify what she loves.

She loves colour, she loves to play creatively, she loves to dance and sing, she loves being outside in all weathers, she loves her partner and children a lot. She loves to cook delicious food and share it with family and friends, she loves to find her own natural rhythms and flow with them, she loves giggling and she loves sharing deep throbbing truth. She loves birdsong and the peace to appreciate it. She loves creating circles for healing and empowerment. She loves the sound of children's play. She loves reading adventures of magic and mystery. She loves to dream of life beyond fear. She loves the feel of her dog's ears, and she loves to open her sock drawer and find her favourite ones there, ready to put on.